Glencoe McGraw-Hill

Chapter 11 Resource Masters

Geometry

Mc Graw Hill Glencoe

Consumable Workbooks Many of the worksheets contained in the Chapter Resource Masters are available as consumable workbooks in both English and Spanish.

	ISBN10	ISBN13
Study Guide and Intervention Workbook	0-07-890848-5	978-0-07-890848-4
Homework Practice Workbook	0-07-890849-3	978-0-07-890849-1

Spanish Version

Homework Practice Workbook	0-07-890853-1	978-0-07-890853-8

Answers for Workbooks The answers for Chapter 11 of these workbooks can be found in the back of this Chapter Resource Masters booklet.

StudentWorks Plus™ This CD-ROM includes the entire Student Edition text along with the English workbooks listed above.

TeacherWorks Plus™ All of the materials found in this booklet are included for viewing, printing, and editing in this CD-ROM.

Spanish Assessment Masters (ISBN10: 0-07-890856-6, ISBN13: 978-0-07-890856-9) These masters contain a Spanish version of Chapter 11 Test Form 2A and Form 2C.

The McGraw-Hill Companies

 Glencoe

Send all inquiries to:
Glencoe/McGraw-Hill
8787 Orion Place
Columbus, OH 43240-4027

ISBN13: 978-0-07-890520-9
ISBN10: 0-07-890520-6

Printed in the United States of America

5 6 7 8 9 10 RHR 14 13

Contents

Teacher's Guide to Using the
Chapter 11 Resource Masters

The *Chapter 11 Resource Masters* includes the core materials needed for Chapter 11. These materials include worksheets, extensions, and assessment options. The answers for these pages appear at the back of this booklet.

All of the materials found in this booklet are included for viewing and printing on the *TeacherWorks Plus™* CD-ROM.

Chapter Resources

Student-Built Glossary (pages 1–2) These masters are a student study tool that presents up to twenty of the key vocabulary terms from the chapter. Students are to record definitions and/or examples for each term. You may suggest that students highlight or star the terms with which they are not familiar. Give this to students before beginning Lesson 11-1. Encourage them to add these pages to their mathematics study notebooks. Remind them to complete the appropriate words as they study each lesson.

Anticipation Guide (pages 3–4) This master, presented in both English and Spanish, is a survey used before beginning the chapter to pinpoint what students may or may not know about the concepts in the chapter. Students will revisit this survey after they complete the chapter to see if their perceptions have changed.

Lesson Resources

Study Guide and Intervention These masters provide vocabulary, key concepts, additional worked-out examples and Check Your Progress exercises to use as a reteaching activity. It can also be used in conjunction with the Student Edition as an instructional tool for students who have been absent.

Skills Practice This master focuses more on the computational nature of the lesson. Use as an additional practice option or as homework for second-day teaching of the lesson.

Practice This master closely follows the types of problems found in the Exercises section of the Student Edition and includes word problems. Use as an additional practice option or as homework for second-day teaching of the lesson.

Word Problem Practice This master includes additional practice in solving word problems that apply the concepts of the lesson. Use as an additional practice or as homework for second-day teaching of the lesson.

Enrichment These activities may extend the concepts of the lesson, offer a historical or multicultural look at the concepts, or widen students' perspectives on the mathematics they are learning. They are written for use with all levels of students.

Graphing Calculator, TI-Nspire, or Spreadsheet Activities These activities present ways in which technology can be used with the concepts in some lessons of this chapter. Use as an alternative approach to some concepts or as an integral part of your lesson presentation.

Assessment Options

The assessment masters in the *Chapter 11 Resource Masters* offer a wide range of assessment tools for formative (monitoring) assessment and summative (final) assessment.

Student Recording Sheet This master corresponds with the standardized test practice at the end of the chapter.

Extended-Response Rubric This master provides information for teachers and students on how to assess performance on open-ended questions.

Quizzes Four free-response quizzes offer assessment at appropriate intervals in the chapter.

Mid-Chapter Test This 1-page test provides an option to assess the first half of the chapter. It parallels the timing of the Mid-Chapter Quiz in the Student Edition and includes both multiple-choice and free-response questions.

Vocabulary Test This test is suitable for all students. It includes a list of vocabulary words and 10 questions to assess students' knowledge of those words. This can also be used in conjunction with one of the leveled chapter tests.

Leveled Chapter Tests

- ***Form 1*** contains multiple-choice questions and is intended for use with approaching grade level students.

- ***Forms 2A and 2B*** contain multiple-choice questions aimed at on grade level students. These tests are similar in format to offer comparable testing situations.

- ***Forms 2C and 2D*** contain free-response questions aimed at on grade level students. These tests are similar in format to offer comparable testing situations.

- ***Form 3*** is a free-response test for use with beyond grade level students.

All of the above mentioned tests include a free-response Bonus question.

Extended-Response Test Performance assessment tasks are suitable for all students. Sample answers and a scoring rubric are included for evaluation.

Standardized Test Practice These three pages are cumulative in nature. It includes three parts: multiple-choice questions with bubble-in answer format, griddable questions with answer grids, and short-answer free-response questions.

Answers

- The answers for the Anticipation Guide and Lesson Resources are provided as reduced pages.
- Full-size answer keys are provided for the assessment masters.

11 Student-Built Glossary

This is an alphabetical list of the key vocabulary terms you will learn in Chapter 11. As you study the chapter, complete each term's definition or description. Remember to add the page number where you found the term. Add these pages to your Geometry Study Notebook to review vocabulary at the end of the chapter.

Vocabulary Term	Found on Page	Definition/Description/Example
apothem		
base of a parallelogram		
base of a triangle		
center of a regular polygon		
central angle of a regular polygon		

(continued on the next page)

11 Student-Built Glossary (continued)

Vocabulary Term	Found on Page	Definition/Description/Example
height of a parallelogram		
height of a trapezoid		
height of a triangle		
radius of a regular polygon		
sector of a circle		

11 Anticipation Guide

Areas of Polygons and Circles

Step 1 *Before you begin Chapter 11*

- Read each statement.
- Decide whether you Agree (A) or Disagree (D) with the statement.
- Write A or D in the first column OR if you are not sure whether you agree or disagree, write NS (Not Sure).

STEP 1 A, D, or NS	Statement	STEP 2 A or D
	1. The area of a parallelogram whose sides measure 5 cm and 9 cm is 5 cm × 9 cm or 45 cm².	
	2. The area of a triangle is one-half its base times its height.	
	3. The area of a kite is the product of its diagonals.	
	4. The area of a rhombus equals half the product of the lengths of its diagonals.	
	5. A segment drawn from the center to a vertex of a regular polygon is called an apothem.	
	6. The formula for the area of a circle is $A = \pi r^2$.	
	7. The area of an irregular figure can be found by separating the figure into shapes with known area formulas.	
	8. If an irregular figure is in the shape of a pentagon, then the formula for the area of a regular pentagon can be used to find its area.	
	9. A sector of a circle with a central angle of 35° will have an area of $\frac{35}{360}\pi r^2$.	
	10. If two polygons are similar, then their areas are proportional to the square of the scale factor between them.	

Step 2 *After you complete Chapter 11*

- Reread each statement and complete the last column by entering an A or a D.
- Did any of your opinions about the statements change from the first column?
- For those statements that you mark with a D, use a piece of paper to write an example of why you disagree.

11 Ejercicios Preparatorios

Áreas de Polígonos y Círculos

Paso 1   *Antes de comenzar el Capítulo 11*

- Lee cada enunciado.
- Decide si estás de acuerdo (A) o en desacuerdo (D) con el enunciado.
- Escribe A o D en la primera columna O si no estás seguro(a) de la respuesta, escribe NS (No estoy seguro(a)).

PASO 1 A, D, o NS	Enunciado	PASO 2 A o D
	1. El área de un paralelogramo con lados 5 cm y 9 cm es 5 cm × 9 cm ó 45 cm².	
	2. El área de un triángulo es la mitad de su base por la altura.	
	3. El área de una cometa es el producto de sus diagonales.	
	4. El área de un rombo es igual a la mitad del producto de las longitudes de sus diagonales.	
	5. Un segmento que se dibuja del centro al vértice de un polígono regular se llama apotema.	
	6. La fórmula para el área de un círculo es $A = \pi r^2$.	
	7. El área de una figura irregular se puede calcular separando la figura en figuras con fórmulas de área conocidas.	
	8. Si una figura irregular tiene forma pentagonal, entonces se puede usar la fórmula del área de un pentágono regular para calcular su área.	
	9. El sector de un círculo con ángulo central de 35° tendrá un área de $\frac{35}{360}\pi r^2$.	
	10. Si dos polígonos son semejantes, entonces sus áreas son proporcionales al cuadrado del factor de escala entre ellos.	

Paso 2   *Después de completar el Capítulo 11*

- Vuelve a leer cada enunciado y completa la última columna con una A o una D.
- ¿Cambió cualquiera de tus opiniones sobre los enunciados de la primera columna?
- En una hoja de papel aparte, escribe un ejemplo de por qué estás en desacuerdo con los enunciados que marcaste con una D.

11-1 Study Guide and Intervention

Areas of Parallelograms and Triangles

Areas of Parallelograms Any side of a parallelogram can be called a **base**. The **height** of a parallelogram is the perpendicular distance between any two parallel bases. The area of a parallelogram is the product of the base and the height.

Area of a Parallelogram	If a parallelogram has an area of A square units, a base of b units, and a height of h units, then $A = bh$.

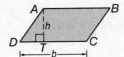

Example   Find the area of parallelogram *EFGH*.

$A = bh$ — Area of a parallelogram

$= 30(18)$ — $b = 30, h = 18$

$= 540$ — Multiply.

The area is 540 square meters.

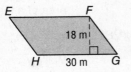

Exercises

Find the perimeter and area of each parallelogram. Round to the nearest tenth if necessary.

1.

2.

3.

4.

5.

6.

7. **TILE FLOOR** A bathroom tile floor is made of black-and-white parallelograms. Each parallelogram is made of two triangles with dimensions as shown. Find the perimeter and area of one parallelogram.

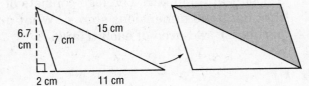

11-1 Study Guide and Intervention (continued)

Areas of Parallelograms and Triangles

Areas Of Triangles The area of a triangle is one half the product of the base and its corresponding height. Like a parallelogram, the base can be any side, and the height is the length of an altitude drawn to a given base.

Area of a Triangle	If a triangle has an area of A square units, a base of b units, and a corresponding height of h units, then $A = \frac{1}{2}bh$.

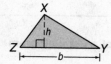

Example **Find the area of the triangle.**

$A = \frac{1}{2}bh$ Area of a triangle

$= \frac{1}{2}(24)(28)$ $b = 24, h = 28$

$= 336$ Multiply.

The area is 336 square meters.

Exercises

Find the perimeter and area of each triangle. Round to the nearest tenth if necessary.

1.

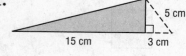

5 cm
15 cm   3 cm

2.

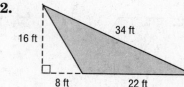

16 ft   34 ft
8 ft   22 ft

3.

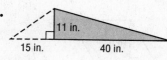

11 in.
15 in.   40 in.

4.

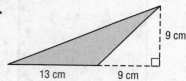

9 cm
13 cm   9 cm

5.

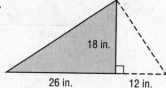

18 in.
26 in.   12 in.

6.

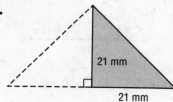

21 mm
21 mm

7. **LOGO** The logo for an engineering company is on a poster at a job fair. The logo consists of two triangles that have the dimensions shown. What are the perimeter and area of each triangle?

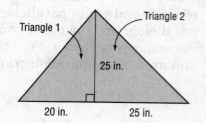

Triangle 1   Triangle 2
25 in.
20 in.   25 in.

11-1 Skills Practice

Areas of Parallelograms and Triangles

Find the perimeter and area of each parallelogram or triangle. Round to the nearest tenth if necessary.

1.

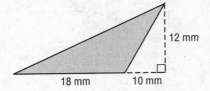

18 mm   10 mm   12 mm

2.

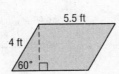

5.5 ft   4 ft   60°

3.

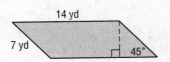

14 yd   7 yd   45°

4.

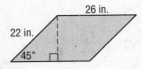

26 in.   22 in.   45°

5.

3.4 m

6.

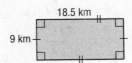

18.5 km   9 km

7.

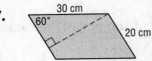

30 cm   60°   20 cm

8.

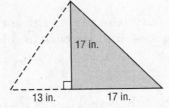

17 in.   13 in.   17 in.

9. The height of a parallelogram is 10 feet more than its base. If the area of the parallelogram is 1200 square feet, find its base and height.

10. The base of a triangle is one half of its height. If the area of the triangle is 196 square millimeters, find its base and height.

Lesson 11-1

11-1 Practice

Areas of Parallelograms and Triangles

Find the perimeter and area of each parallelogram or triangle. Round to the nearest tenth if necessary.

1.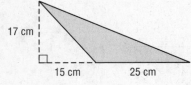
5 m
60°
11 m

2.
8 cm
45°
10 cm

3.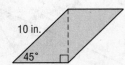
10 in.
45°

4.
17 cm
15 cm   25 cm

5.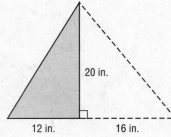
20 in.
12 in.   16 in.

6.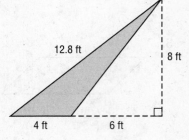
12.8 ft   8 ft
4 ft   6 ft

7. The height of a parallelogram is 5 feet more than its base. If the area of the parallelogram is 204 square feet, find its base and height.

8. The height of a parallelogram is three times its base. If the area of the parallelogram is 972 square inches, find its base and height.

9. The base of a triangle is four times its height. If the area of the triangle is 242 square millimeters, find its base and height.

10. **FRAMING** A rectangular poster measures 42 inches by 26 inches. A frame shop fitted the poster with a half-inch mat border.

    a. Find the area of the poster.

    b. Find the area of the mat border.

    c. Suppose the wall is marked where the poster will hang. The marked area includes an additional 12-inch space around the poster and frame. Find the total wall area that has been marked for the poster.

11-1 Word Problem Practice

Areas of Parallelograms and Triangles

1. PACKAGING A box with a square opening is squashed into the rhombus shown below.

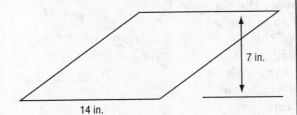

What is the area of the opening?

2. RUNNING Jason jogs once around a city block shaped like a parallelogram.

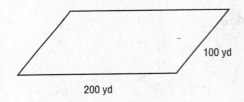

How far did Jason jog?

3. SHADOWS A rectangular billboard casts a shadow on the ground in the shape of a parallelogram. What is the area of the ground covered by the shadow? Round your answer to the nearest tenth.

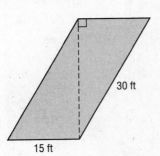

4. PATHS A concrete path shown below is made by joining several parallelograms.

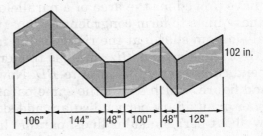

What is the total area of the path?

5. HIGHWAY SUPPORTS Three columns are being placed at the vertices of a right triangle to support a highway. Two of the columns are marked on the coordinate plane shown.

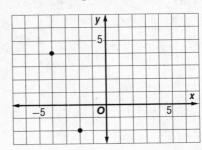

a. What are two possible locations of the third column to form a right triangle?

b. What is the area in square units of each of the two right triangles that result from the possibilities you found in part **a**? Explain.

Lesson 11-1

11-1 Enrichment

Area of a Parallelogram

You can prove some interesting results using the formula you have proved for the area of a parallelogram by drawing auxiliary lines to form congruent regions. Consider the top parallelogram shown at the right. In the figure, d is the length of the diagonal $\overline{BD}$, and k is the length of the perpendicular segment from A to $\overline{BD}$. Now consider the second figure, which shows the same parallelogram with a number of auxiliary perpendiculars added. Use what you know about perpendicular lines, parallel lines, and congruent triangles to answer the following.

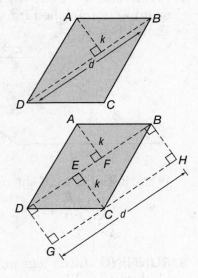

1. What kind of figure is $DBHG$?

2. If you moved $\triangle AFB$ to the lower-left end of figure $DBHG$, would it fit perfectly on top of $\triangle DGC$? Explain your answer.

3. Which two triangular pieces of $\square ABCD$ are congruent to $\triangle CBH$?

4. The area of $\square ABCD$ is the same as that of figure $DBHG$, since the pieces of $\square ABCD$ can be rearranged to form $DBHG$. Express the area of $\square ABCD$ in terms of the measurements k and d.

11-1 Graphing Calculator Activity

Cabri Junior: Areas of Parallelograms

Cabri Junior can be used to find the perimeters and areas of parallelograms.

Step 1 Draw a parallelogram.
- Select **F2 Segment** to draw a segment.
- Select **F5 Alph-num** to label the endpoints of the segment A and B.
- Draw segment AD.
- Select **F3 Parallel** to draw a line parallel to segment AB through D. Select point D, and then segment AB.
- Draw a line parallel to segment AD through B.
- Select **F2 Point, Intersection** to place a point at the intersection of the two lines drawn. Label the point C.
- Select **F2 Quad** and draw a quadrilateral by selecting points A, B, C, and D.

Step 2 Find the measure of the area of parallelogram $ABCD$.
- Select **F5 Measure, Area.**
- Place the cursor on any segment of parallelogram $ABCD$. Then press ENTER.
- The area appears with the hand attached. Move the number to an appropriate place.

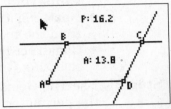

Step 3 Find the measure of the perimeter of parallelogram $ABCD$.
- Select **F5 Measure, D. & Length.**
- Place the cursor on any segment of parallelogram $ABCD$. Then press ENTER.
- The area appears with the hand attached. Move the number to an appropriate place.

The perimeter of the parallelogram shown here is 16.2 units and the area is 13.8 square units.

Exercises

Analyze your drawing.

1. Find the lengths of all four sides of the parallelogram.

2. Using the information from Exercise 1, what is the perimeter of the parallelogram? Does this measurement match that found by Cabri Junior?

3. Construct a line segment showing the height of the parallelogram. What is the length of the line segment?

4. What is the measure of the base of the parallelogram?

5. Using the information from Exercises 3 and 4, what is the area of the parallelogram? Does this measurement match the one found by Cabri Junior?

6. Select one of the vertices and drag it to change the dimensions of the parallelogram. (Press CLEAR so the pointer becomes a black arrow. Move the pointer close to a vertex until the arrow becomes transparent and the vertex is blinking. Press ALPHA to change the arrow to a hand. Then move the vertex.) Do you see any patterns or relationships?

Lesson 11-1

11-1   Geometer's Sketchpad Activity

Areas of Parallelograms

The Geometer's Sketchpad can be used to find the perimeters and areas of parallelograms.

Step 1   Use The Geometer's Sketchpad to draw a parallelogram.
  • Construct a segment by selecting the Segment tool from the toolbar. First, click the first point. Then click on a second point to draw the segment.
  • Next, use one of the endpoints of the original segment as the first point for the new segment and click on a second point to construct the new segment.
  • Construct a parallel line to the original segment by first highlighting the original segment and the endpoint not on that segment. Then select **Parallel Line** from the **Construct** menu.
  • Construct a parallel line to the second segment by highlighting the second segment and the point not on it. Then select **Parallel Line** from the **Construct** menu.
  • Next, construct a point on the intersection of the two lines. Use the Point tool from the toolbar to select the point where the two lines intersect.
  • Construct the interior of the parallelogram by highlighting all four points and selecting **Quadrilateral Interior** under the **Construct** menu.

Step 2   Use The Geometer's Sketchpad to find the perimeter of the parallelogram.
  • Highlight the interior of the parallelogram using the Selection Arrow tool from the toolbar.
  • Next, find the perimeter by selecting **Perimeter** under the **Measure** menu.

Step 3   Use The Geometer's Sketchpad to find the area of the parallelogram.
  • Highlight the interior of the parallelogram using the Selection Arrow tool from the toolbar.
  • Next, find the area by selecting **Area** under the **Measure** menu.

The perimeter of the parallelogram shown here is 11.33 cm and the area is 6.63 cm².

Exercises

Analyze your drawing.

1. Find the lengths of all four sides of the parallelogram.
2. Using the information from Exercise 1, what is the perimeter of the parallelogram? Does this measurement match that found by the Geometer's Sketchpad?
3. Construct a line segment showing the height of the parallelogram. What is the length of the line segment?
4. What is the measure of the base of the parallelogram?
5. Using the information from Exercises 3 and 4, what is the area of the parallelogram? Does this measurement match the one found by the Geometer's Sketchpad?
6. Select one of the vertices and drag it to change the dimensions of the parallelogram. Do you see any patterns or relationships?

11-2 Study Guide and Intervention

Areas of Trapezoids, Rhombi, and Kites

Areas of Trapezoids A trapezoid is a quadrilateral with exactly one pair of parallel sides, called bases. The **height of a trapezoid** is the perpendicular distance between the bases. The area of a trapezoid is the product of one half the height and the sum of the lengths of the bases.

Area of a Trapezoid	If a trapezoid has an area of A square units, bases of b_1 and b_2 units, and a height of h units, then $A = \frac{1}{2}h(b_1 + b_2)$	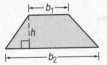

Example Find the area of the trapezoid.

$A = \frac{1}{2}h(b_1 + b_2)$ Area of a trapezoid

$= \frac{1}{2}(15)(18 + 40)$ $h = 15$, $b_1 = 18$, and $b_2 = 40$

$= 435$ Simplify.

The area of the trapezoid is 435 square meters.

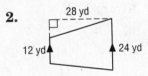

Exercises

Find the area of each trapezoid.

1.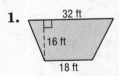
   32 ft / 16 ft / 18 ft

2. 28 yd / 12 yd / 24 yd

3. 32 m / 20 m / 50 m

4. 5 in. / 8 in. / 15 in.

5.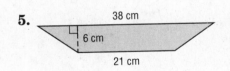
   38 cm / 6 cm / 21 cm

6. 30 ft / 16 ft / 18 ft

7. **OPEN ENDED** Ryan runs a landscaping business. A new customer has a trapezodial shaped backyard, shown at the right. How many square feet of grass will Ryan have to mow?

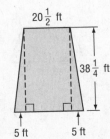
$20\frac{1}{2}$ ft / $38\frac{1}{4}$ ft / 5 ft / 5 ft

Lesson 11-2

11-2 Study Guide and Intervention *(continued)*

Areas of Trapezoids, Rhombi, and Kites

Areas of Rhombi and Kites A rhombus is a parallelogram with all four sides congruent. A kite is a quadrilateral with exactly two pairs of consecutive sides congruent.

Area of Rhombus or Kite	If a rhombus or kite has an area of A square units, and diagonals of d_1 and d_2 units, then $A = \frac{1}{2} d_1 \cdot d_2$.

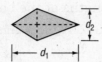

Example **Find the area of the rhombus.**

$A = \frac{1}{2} d_1 d_2$ Area of rhombus

$= \frac{1}{2} (7)(9)$ $d_1 = 7$, and $d_2 = 9$

$= 31.5$ Simplify.

The area is 31.5 square meters.

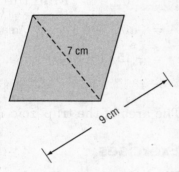

Exercises

Find the area of each rhombus or kite.

1.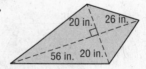

2.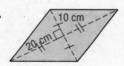

3.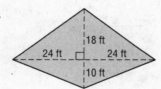

4.

5.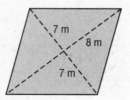

6.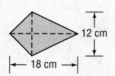

ALGEBRA Find x.

7. $A = 164$ ft²

8. $A = 340$ cm²

9. $A = 247.5$ mm²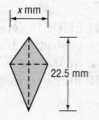

11-2 Skills Practice

Areas of Trapezoids, Rhombi, and Kites

Find the area of each trapezoid, rhombus, or kite.

1.
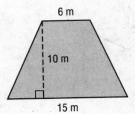
6 m
10 m
15 m

2.
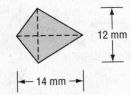
12 mm
14 mm

3.
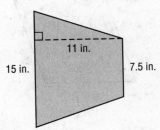
11 in.
15 in.   7.5 in.

4.
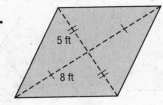
5 ft
8 ft

5.
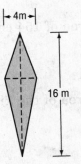
4m
16 m

6.
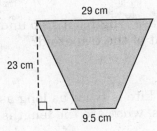
29 cm
23 cm
9.5 cm

ALGEBRA Find each missing length.

7. A trapezoid has base lengths of 6 and 15 centimeters with an area of 136.5 square centimeters. What is the height of the trapezoid?

8. One diagonal of a kite is four times as long as the other diagonal. If the area of the kite is 72 square meters, what are the lengths of the diagonals?

9. A trapezoid has a height of 24 meters, a base of 4 meters, and an area of 264 square meters. What is the length of the other base?

Lesson 11-2

11-2 Practice

Areas of Trapezoids, Rhombi, and Kites

Find the area of each trapezoid, rhombus, or kite.

1.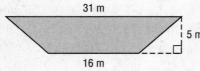
31 m
5 m
16 m

2.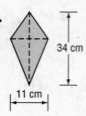
34 cm
11 cm

3.
2.4 in.
16.4 in.

4.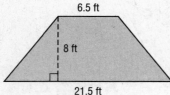
6.5 ft
8 ft
21.5 ft

5.
17 ft
12 ft

6.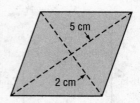
5 cm
2 cm

ALGEBRA Find each missing length.

7. A trapezoid has base lengths of 19.5 and 24.5 centimeters with an area of 154 cm². What is the height of the trapezoid?

8. One diagonal of a kite is twice as long as the other diagonal. If the area of the kite is 400 square meters, what are the lengths of the diagonals?

9. A trapezoid has a height of 40 inches, a base of 15 inches, and an area of 2400 square inches. What is the length of the other base?

10. **DESIGN** Mr. Hagarty used 16 congruent rhombi-shaped tiles to design the midsection of the backsplash area above a kitchen sink. The length of the design is 27 inches and the total area is 108 square inches.

   a. Find the area of one rhombus.

   b. Find the length of each diagonal.

11-2 Word Problem Practice

Areas of Trapezoids, Rhombi, and Kites

1. **INTERIOR DESIGN** The 20-by-20-foot square shows an office floor plan composed of three indoor gardens and one walkway, all congruent in shape. The gardens are centered around a 15-by-15 foot lounging area. What is the area of one of these gardens?

4. **HEXAGONS** Heather makes a hexagon by attaching two trapezoids together as shown. What is the area of the hexagon?

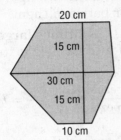

2. **CUTOUTS** A trapezoid is cut from a 6-inch-by-2-inch rectangle. The length of one base is 6 inches. What is the area of the trapezoid?

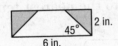

5. **TILINGS** Tile making often requires an artist to find clever ways of dividing a shape into several smaller, congruent shapes. Consider the isosceles trapezoid shown below.

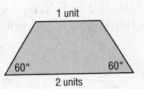

a. Show how to divide the trapezoid into 3 congruent triangles. What is the area of each triangle?

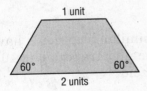

3. **SHARING** Bernard has a birthday cake shaped like a kite. He needs to cut it into four pieces to share with three friends. He divides the cake as shown below. Which piece(s) is the largest? What is the area of the cake?

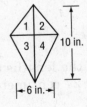

b. Show how to divide the trapezoid into 4 congruent trapezoids. What is the area of each of the smaller trapezoids?

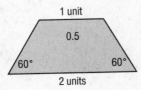

Lesson 11-2

11-2 Enrichment

Perimeters of Similar Figures

You have learned that if two figures are similar, the ratio of the lengths of the corresponding sides are equal. If two figures are similar, then their perimeters are also proportional to the scale factor between them.

Trapezoid II is k times larger than trapezoid I. Thus, its base is k times as large as that of trapezoid I and its height its k times as large as that of trapezoid I.

$$\frac{\text{side of trapezoid II}}{\text{side of trapezoid I}} = \frac{ks_2}{s_2} = k$$

$$\frac{\text{perimeter trapezoid II}}{\text{perimeter trapezoid I}} = \frac{k(s_1 + s_2 + b_1 + b_2)}{s_1 + s_2 + b_1 + b_2} = k$$

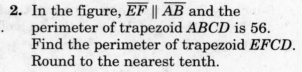

Trapezoid I
Perimeter = $s_1 + s_2 + b_1 + b_2$

Trapezoid II
Perimeter = $ks_1 + ks_2 + kb_1 + kb_2$
= $k(s_1 + s_2 + b_1 + b_2)$

Solve.

1. Trapezoid $ABCD$ ~ trapezoid $EFGH$.
   $EF = 10$, $GH = 8$, $HE = GF = 5$, and $AB = 5$.
   Find the perimeter of trapezoid $ABCD$.

2. In the figure, $\overline{EF} \parallel \overline{AB}$ and the perimeter of trapezoid $ABCD$ is 56. Find the perimeter of trapezoid $EFCD$. Round to the nearest tenth.

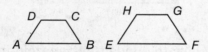

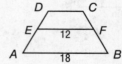

3. Two similar trapezoids have perimeters of 37.5 feet and 150 feet. The length of a side of the smaller trapezoid is 10 feet. Find the length of the corresponding side of the larger trapezoid.

4. Find the ratio of the perimeters of two similar trapezoids if the lengths of two corresponding sides of the trapezoids are 9 centimeters and 27 centimeters.

11-3 Study Guide and Intervention

Areas of Circles and Sectors

Areas Of Circles The area of a circle is equal to π times the square of radius.

Area of a Circle	If a circle has an area of A square units and a radius of r units, then $A = \pi r^2$.

Example **Find the area of the circle p.**

$A = \pi r^2$ Area of a circle

$= \pi(6)^2$ $r = 6$

≈ 113.1 Use a calculator.

The area of the circle is about 113.1 square meters.

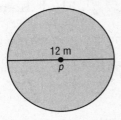

If $d = 12$ m, then $r = 6$ m.

Exercises

Find the area of each circle. Round to the nearest tenth.

1.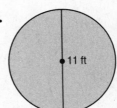

2.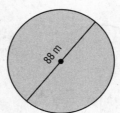

3.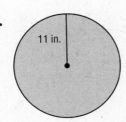

4.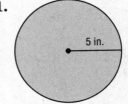

5.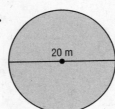

6.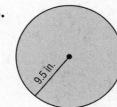

Find the indicated measure. Round to the nearest tenth.

7. The area of a circle is 153.9 square centimeters. Find the diameter.

8. Find the diameter of a circle with an area of 490.9 square millimeters.

9. The area of a circle is 907.9 square inches. Find the radius.

10. Find the radius of a circle with an area of 63.6 square feet.

Lesson 11-3

11-3　Study Guide and Intervention (continued)

Areas of Circles and Sectors

Areas of Sectors A sector of a circle is a region bounded by a central angle and its intercepted arc.

Area of a Sector	If a sector of a circle has an area of A square units, a central angle measuring $x°$, and a radius of r units, then $A = \frac{x}{360}\pi r^2$.

Example **Find the area of the shaded sector.**

$A = \dfrac{x}{360} \cdot \pi r^2$ 　Area of a sector

$ = \dfrac{36}{360} \cdot \pi(5)^2$ 　$x = 36$ and $r = 5$

$ \approx 7.85$ 　　Use a calculator.

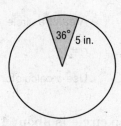

The area of the sector is about 7.85 square inches.

Exercises

Find the area of each shaded sector. Round to the nearest tenth.

1.
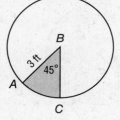

2.
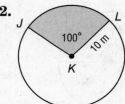

3.
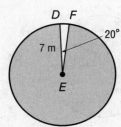

4.
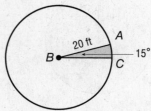

5.
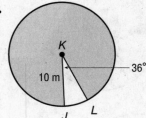

6.
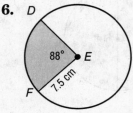

7. **SANDWICHES** For a party, Samantha wants to have finger sandwiches. She cuts sandwiches into circles. If she cuts each circle into three congruent pieces, what is the area of each piece?

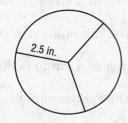

11-3 Skills Practice

Areas of Circles and Sectors

Find the area of each circle.

1.

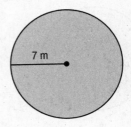

7 m

2.

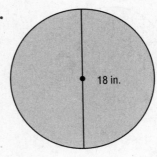

18 in.

3.

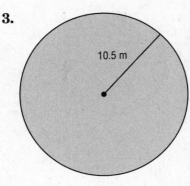

10.5 m

Find the indicated measure. Round to the nearest tenth.

4. The area of a circle is 132.7 square centimeters. Find the diameter.

5. Find the diameter of a circle with an area of 1134.1 square millimeters.

6. The area of a circle is 706.9 square inches. Find the radius.

7. Find the radius of a circle with an area of 2827.4 square feet.

Find the area of each shaded sector. Round to the nearest tenth.

8.

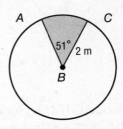

A   C
51°
2 m
B

9.

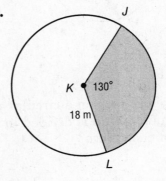

J
K 130°
18 m
L

10.

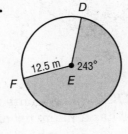

D
12.5 m 243°
F   E

11. **GAMES** Jason wants to make a spinner for a new board game he invented. The spinner is a circle divided into 8 congruent pieces, what is the area of each piece to the nearest tenth?

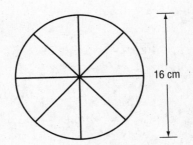

16 cm

Lesson 11-3

11-3 Practice

Areas of Circles and Sectors

Find the area of each circle. Round to the nearest tenth.

1.
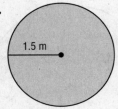
1.5 m

2.
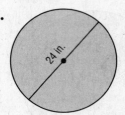
24 in.

3.
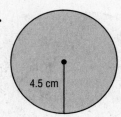
4.5 cm

Find the indicated measure. Round to the nearest tenth.

4. The area of a circle is 3.14 square centimeters. Find the diameter.

5. Find the diameter of a circle with an area of 855.3 square millimeters.

6. The area of a circle is 201.1 square inches. Find the radius.

7. Find the radius of a circle with an area of 2290.2 square feet.

Find the area of each shaded sector. Round to the nearest tenth.

8.
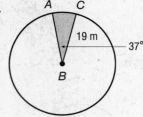
A   C
19 m
37°
B

9.
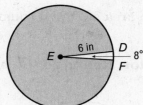
6 in   D
E   8°
F

10.
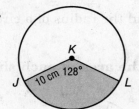
K
J 10 cm 128° L

11. **CLOCK** Sadie wants to draw a clock face on a circular piece of cardboard. If the clock face has a diameter of 20 centimeters and is divided into congruent pieces so that each sector is 30°, what is the area of each piece?

11-3 Word Problem Practice

Areas of Circles and Sectors

1. LOBBY The lobby of a bank features a large marble circular table. The diameter of the circle is 15 feet.

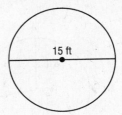

15 ft

What is the area of the circular table? Round your answer to the nearest tenth.

2. PORTHOLES A circular window on a ship has a radius of 8 inches. What is the area of the window? Round your answer to the nearest hundredth.

3. PEACE SYMBOL The symbol below, a circle separated into 3 equal sectors, has come to symbolize peace.

r

Suppose the circle has radius r. What is the area of each sector?

4. SOUP CAN Julie needs to cover the top and bottom of a can of soup with construction paper to include in her art project. Each circle has a diameter of 7.5 centimeters. What is the total area of the can that Julie must cover?

5. POOL A circular pool is surrounded by a circular sidewalk. The circular sidewalk is 3 feet wide. The diameter of the sidewalk and pool is 26 feet.

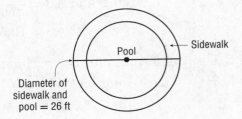

Pool   ← Sidewalk

Diameter of sidewalk and pool = 26 ft

a. What is the diameter of the pool?

b. What is the area of the sidewalk and pool?

c. What is the area of the pool?

Lesson 11-3

11-3 Enrichment

Perimeter of a Sector

You have learned how to find the area of a sector of a circle using a ratio of the circle and the area formula. Now you will learn how to find the perimeter of the sector of the circle.

The perimeter of the sector is the sum of the lengths of two radii and the length of its arc.

$P_{sector} = 2r + $ length of $\widehat{AB}$

Step 1 Find the length of $\widehat{AB}$.

The length of the arc is a section of the circumference. Multiply the ratio of the degree measure of the intercepted arc to 360° by the circumference of the circle.

$$\text{Length of arc} = \frac{x}{360} \cdot 2(\pi)(r)$$

$$\text{Length of } \widehat{AB} = \frac{100}{360} \cdot 2(\pi)(6)$$ $x = 100$ and $r = 6$

$$\approx 10.5$$ Use a calculator.

Step 2 Use the formula for the perimeter of a sector.

$P_{sector} = 2r + $ length of $\widehat{AB}$

$$\approx 2(6) + 10.5$$

$$\approx 22.5$$

The perimeter of the sector is about 22.5 inches.

Exercises

Find the perimeter of the shaded sector. Round to the nearest tenth.

1.

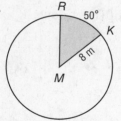

2.

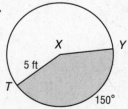

3.

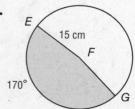

4.

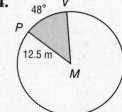

11-4 Study Guide and Intervention

Areas of Regular Polygons and Composite Figures

Areas of Regular Polygons In a regular polygon, the segment drawn from the center of the polygon perpendicular to the opposite side is called the **apothem**. In the figure at the right, $\overline{AP}$ is the apothem and $\overline{AR}$ is the radius of the circumscribed circle.

Area of a Regular Polygon	If a regular polygon has an area of A square units, a perimeter of P units, and an apothem of a units, then $A = \frac{1}{2}aP$.

Example 1 **Verify the formula** $A = \frac{1}{2}aP$ **for the regular pentagon above.**

For $\triangle RAS$, the area is
$A = \frac{1}{2}bh = \frac{1}{2}(RS)(AP)$. So the area of the pentagon is $A = 5\left(\frac{1}{2}\right)(RS)(AP)$. Substituting P for $5RS$ and substituting a for AP, then $A = \frac{1}{2}aP$.

Example 2 **Find the area of regular pentagon $RSTUV$ above if its perimeter is 60 centimeters.**

First find the apothem.
The measure of central angle RAS is $\frac{360°}{5}$ or $72°$. Therefore, $m\angle RAP = 36$. The perimeter is 60, so $RS = 12$ and $RP = 6$.

$$\tan m\angle RAP = \frac{RP}{AP}$$
$$\tan 36° = \frac{6}{AP}$$
$$AP = \frac{6}{\tan 36°}$$
$$\approx 8.26$$

So, $A = \frac{1}{2}aP = \frac{1}{2}(60)(8.26)$ or 247.8.
The area is about 248 square centimeters.

Exercises

Find the area of each regular polygon. Round to the nearest tenth.

1.
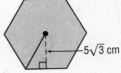
14 m

2.

10 in.

3.
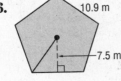
15 in.

4.

$5\sqrt{3}$ cm

5.

10 in.

6.

10.9 m
7.5 m

Lesson 11-4

11-4 Study Guide and Intervention (continued)

Areas of Regular Polygons and Composite Figures

Areas of Composite Figures A composite figure is a figure that can be seprated into regions that are basic figures. To find the area of a composite figure, separate the figure into basic figures of which we can find the area. The sum of the areas of the basic figures is the area of the figure.

Example **Find the area of the shaded region.**

a.

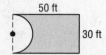

The figure is a rectangle minus one half of a circle. The radius of the circle is one half of 30 or 15.

$$A = lw - \frac{1}{2}\pi r^2$$
$$= 50(30) - 0.5\pi(15)^2$$
$$\approx 1146.6 \text{ or about } 1147 \text{ ft}^2$$

b.

The dimensions of the rectangle are 10 centimeters and 30 centimeters. The area of the shaded region is

$$(10)(30) - 3\pi(5^2) = 300 - 75\pi$$
$$\approx 64.4 \text{ cm}^2$$

Exercises

Find the area of each figure. Round to the nearest tenth if necessary.

1.

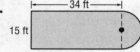

2.

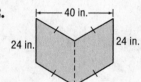

3.

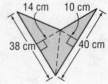

4.

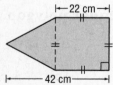

5.

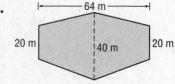

6.

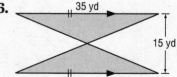

11-4 **Skills Practice**

Areas of Regular Polygons and Composite Figures

Find the area of each regular polygon. Round to the nearest tenth.

1.

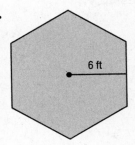

8 m

2.

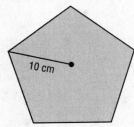

10 cm

3.

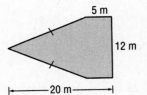

6 ft

4.

15 in.

Find the area of each figure. Round to the nearest tenth if necessary.

5.

5 m
12 m
20 m

6.

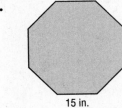

3 ft
7 ft

7.

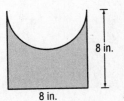

8 in.
8 in.

8.

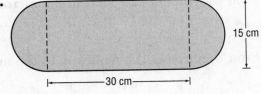

15 cm
30 cm

11-4 Practice

Areas of Regular Polygons and Composite Figures

Find the area of each regular polygon. Round to the nearest tenth.

1.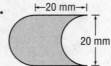
14 cm

2.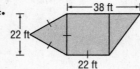
7 m

Find the area of each figure. Round to the nearest tenth if necessary.

3.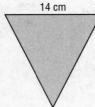
|—20 mm—|
20 mm

4.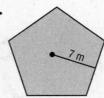
|— 38 ft —|
22 ft
22 ft

5.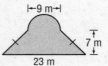
|—9 m—|
7 m
23 m

6.
|—20 in.—|
13 in. 30 in.
13 in.

7. LANDSCAPING One of the displays at a botanical garden is a koi pond with a walkway around it. The figure shows the dimensions of the pond and the walkway.

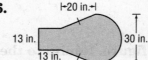
7 ft
15 ft
|—13 ft—|
|——— 35 ft ———|

a. Find the area of the pond to the nearest tenth.

b. Find the area of the walkway to the nearest tenth.

11-4 Word Problem Practice

Areas of Regular Polygons and Composite Figures

1. YIN-YANG SYMBOL A well-known symbol from Chinese culture is the yin-yang symbol, shown below.

Suppose the large circle has radius r, the small circles have radius $\frac{r}{8}$, and the S-curve is two semicircles, each with radius $\frac{r}{2}$. In terms of r, what is the area of the black region?

2. PYRAMIDS Martha's clubhouse is shaped like a square pyramid with four congruent equilateral triangles for its sides. All of the edges are 6 feet long. What is the total surface area of the clubhouse including the floor? Round your answer to the nearest hundredth.

3. MINIATURE GOLF The plan for a miniature golf hole is shown below. The right angle in the drawing is a central angle.

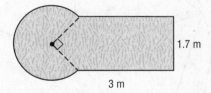

1.7 m

3 m

What is the area of the playing surface? Round your answer to the nearest hundredth of a square meter.

4. TRACK A running track has an inner and outer edge. Both the inner and outer edges consist of two semicircles joined by two straight line segments. The straight line segments are 100 yards long. The radii of the inner edge semicircles are 25 yards each and the radii of the outer edge semicircles are 32 yards each. What is the area of the track? Round your answer to the nearest hundredth of a yard.

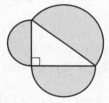

100 yd
25 yd

5. SEMICIRCLES Bridget arranged three semicircles in the pattern shown.

The right triangle has side lengths 6, 8, and 10 inches.

a. What is the total area of the three semicircles? Round your answer to the nearest hundredth of a square inch.

b. If the right triangle had side lengths $\sqrt{21}$, $\sqrt{79}$, and 10 inches, what would the total area of the three semicircles be? Round your answer to the nearest hundredth of a square inch.

Lesson 11-4

11-4   Enrichment

Areas of Inscribed Polygons

A protractor can be used to inscribe a regular polygon in a circle.
Follow the steps below to inscribe a regular nonagon in ⊙N.

Step 1 Find the degree measure of each of
the nine congruent arcs.

Step 2 Draw 9 radii to form 9 angles with
the measure you found in Step 1.
The radii will intersect the circle in
9 points.

Step 3 Connect the nine points to form the
nonagon.

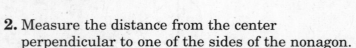

1. Find the length of one side of the
nonagon to the nearest tenth of a
centimeter. What is the perimeter of
the nonagon?

2. Measure the distance from the center
perpendicular to one of the sides of the nonagon.

3. What is the area of one of the nine triangles formed?

4. What is the area of the nonagon?

Make the appropriate changes in Steps 1–3 above to inscribe
a regular pentagon in ⊙P. Answer each of the following.

5. Use a protractor to inscribe a
regular pentagon in ⊙P.

6. What is the measure of each of
the five congruent arcs?

7. What is the perimeter of the
pentagon to the nearest tenth
of a centimeter?

8. What is the area of the pentagon
to the nearest tenth of a
centimeter?

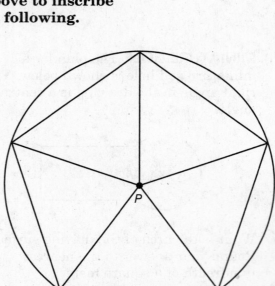

11-5 Study Guide and Intervention

Areas of Similar Figures

Areas of Similar Figures If two polygons are similar, then their areas are proportional to the square of the scale factor between them.

Example $\triangle JKL \sim \triangle PQR$.
The area of $\triangle JKL$ is 40 square inches.
Find the area of $\triangle PQR$.

Find the scale factor: $\frac{12}{10}$ or $\frac{6}{5}$.

The ratio of their areas is $\left(\frac{6}{5}\right)^2$.

$\dfrac{\text{area of } \triangle PQR}{\text{area of} \triangle JKL} = \left(\frac{6}{5}\right)^2$ Write a proportion.

$\dfrac{\text{area of } \triangle PQR}{40} = \dfrac{36}{25}$ Area of $\triangle JKL = 40$; $\left(\frac{6}{5}\right)^2 = \frac{36}{25}$

$\text{area of } \triangle PQR = \dfrac{36}{25} \cdot 40$ Multiply each side by 40.

$\text{area of } \triangle PQR = 57.6$ Simplify.

So the area of $\triangle PQR$ is 57.6 square inches.

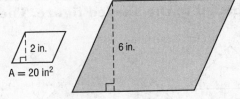

Exercises

For each pair of similar figures, find the area of the shaded figure. Round to the nearest tenth if necessary.

1.

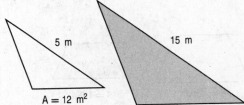

5 m   15 m   A = 12 m²

2.

2 in.   6 in.   A = 20 in²

3.

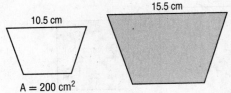

10.5 cm   15.5 cm   A = 200 cm²

4.

20 ft   16 ft   A = 8050 ft²

Lesson 11-5

11-5   **Study Guide and Intervention** (continued)

Areas of Similar Figures

Scale Factors and Missing Measures in Similar Figures You can use the areas of similar figures to find the scale factor between them or a missing measure.

Example If □*ABDC* is similar to □*FGJH*, find the value of *x*.

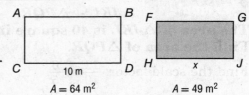

Let *k* be the scale factor between □*ABDC* and □*FGJH*.

$$\frac{\text{area } \square ABCD}{\text{area } \square FGJH} = k^2 \qquad \text{Theorem 11.1}$$

$$\frac{64}{49} = k^2 \qquad \text{Substitution}$$

$$\frac{8}{7} = k \qquad \text{Take the positive square root of each side.}$$

Use this scale factor to find the value of *x*.

$$\frac{CD}{HJ} = k \qquad \text{The ratio of corresponding lengths of similar polygons is equal to the scale factor between the polygons.}$$

$$\frac{10}{x} = \frac{8}{7} \qquad \text{Substitution}$$

$$x = \frac{7}{8} \cdot 10 \text{ or } 8.75 \qquad \text{Multiply each side by 10.}$$

Exercises

For each pair of similar figures, use the given areas to find the scale factor from the unshaded to the shaded figure. Then find *x*.

1.

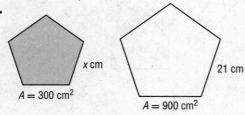

A = 54 in²   A = 216 in²

2.

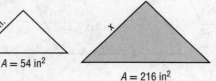 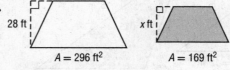

28 ft   A = 296 ft²   x ft   A = 169 ft²

3.

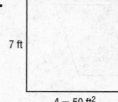

A = 300 cm²   x cm   A = 900 cm²   21 cm

4.

7 ft   A = 50 ft²   x   A = 30 ft²

11-5 Skills Practice

Areas of Similar Figures

For each pair of similar figures, find the area of the shaded figure.

1.

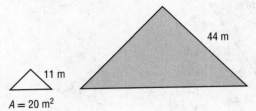

44 m

11 m

$A = 20 \text{ m}^2$

2.

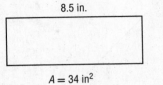

8.5 in.

2 in.

$A = 34 \text{ in}^2$

For each pair of similar figures, use the given areas to find the scale factor from the unshaded to the shaded figure. Then find x.

3. 21 m

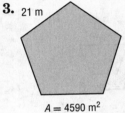

x

$A = 4590 \text{ m}^2$ $A = 510 \text{ m}^2$

4. 12 ft x

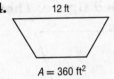

$A = 360 \text{ ft}^2$

$A = 10 \text{ ft}^2$

5.

x

9.5 in.

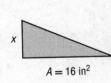   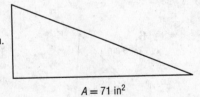

$A = 16 \text{ in}^2$ $A = 71 \text{ in}^2$

6.

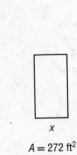

14 ft x

$A = 588 \text{ ft}^2$ $A = 272 \text{ ft}^2$

7. SCIENCE PROJECT Matt has two posters for his science project. Each poster is a rectangle. The length of the larger poster is 11 inches. The length of the smaller poster is 6 inches. What is the area of the smaller poster if the larger poster is 93.5 square inches?

Lesson 11-5

11-5 Practice

Areas of Similar Figures

For each pair of similar figures, find the area of the shaded figure.

1.

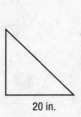 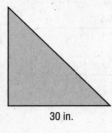

20 in.   30 in.

$A = 200$ in^2

2.

16 m

3 m

$A = 38$ m^2

For each pair of similar figures, use the given areas to find the scale factor from the unshaded to the shaded figure. Then find *x*.

3.

 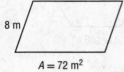

x m   8 m

$A = 50$ m^2 $A = 72$ m^2

4.

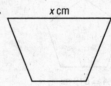

x cm   7 cm

$A = 70$ cm^2 $A = 30$ cm^2

5.

x ft   8 ft

$A = 16$ ft^2

$A = 64$ ft^2

6.

9 cm   *x* cm

$A = 39$ cm^2 $A = 13$ cm^2

7. ARCHERY A target consists of two concentric similar octagons. The outside octagon has a side length of 2 feet and an area of 19.28 square feet. If the inside octagon has a side length of 1.5 feet, what is the area of the inside octagon?

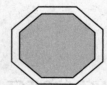

11-5 Word Problem Practice

Areas of Similar Figures

1. CHANGING DIMENSIONS A polygon has an area of 225 square meters. If the area is tripled, how does each side length change?

2. CAKE Smith's Bakery is baking several large cakes for a community festival. The cakes consist of two geometrically similar shapes as shown. If 50 pieces of cake can be cut from the smaller cake, how many pieces of the same size can be cut from the larger cake? Round to the nearest piece of cake.

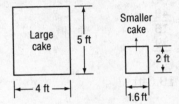

3. PINS Carla has a shirt with decorative pins in the shape of equilateral triangles. The pins come in two sizes. The larger pin has a side length that is three times longer than the smaller pin. If the area of the smaller pin is 6.9 square centimeters, what is the approximate area of the larger pin?

4. FOUNTAIN A local park has two fountains in the shape of similar trapezoids as shown.

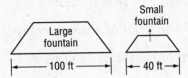

A cement company charges $1000 to pour the cement needed to go under the smaller fountain. How much should the town budget for the cement for both fountains? Explain.

5. SCULPTURE An artist creates metal sculptures in the shape of regular octagons. The side length of the larger sculpture is 7 inches, and the area of the base of the smaller sculpture is 19.28 square inches.

a. What is the side length of the smaller sculpture?

b. The artist is going to pack the sculptures in a circular box to take them to an art show. Will the larger sculpture fit in a circular box with a 15-inch diameter? Explain your reasoning.

Lesson 11-5

11-5 Enrichment

Areas of Similar Figures You have learned that to find the area of a composite figure, you find the area of each basic figure and then use the Area Addition Postulate. You have also learned that if two figures are similar, then their areas are proportional to the square of the scale factor between them.

You can find the area of similar composite figures using this knowledge.

Find the area of composite figure B.

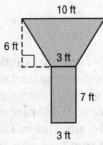

Step 1: Find the area of composite figure A.

Area of rectangle = (3 ft)(7 ft) = 21 ft²

Area of trapezoid = $\frac{1}{2}$ (6 ft)(10 ft + 3 ft) = 39 ft²

Area of composite figure A = 21 ft² + 39 ft² = 60 ft².

Step 2: Use scale factor to find the area of composite figure B.

$$\frac{\text{area composite figure A}}{\text{area composite figure B}} = \left(\frac{7}{4}\right)^2$$

$$= \frac{49}{16}$$

$$\frac{60 \text{ ft}^2}{\text{area composite figure B}} = \frac{49}{16}$$

area composite figure B = $60 \cdot \frac{16}{49} = 19.6$ ft²

So the area of composite figure B is about 19.6 square feet.

Solve.

1. Composite figure A is similar to composite figure B. Find the area of composite figure B.

12 in.
6 in.
10 in.
14 in.
A
21 in.
B

2. Jim is making a scale model of his rectangular backyard and circular pool. If the scale factor is 1:20, what is the area of his model?

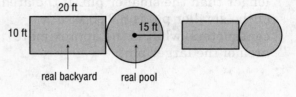

20 ft
10 ft
15 ft
real backyard   real pool

3. Composite figure A is similar to composite figure B. Find the value of x in composite figure B.

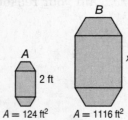

B
A
x
2 ft
$A = 124$ ft² $A = 1116$ ft²

4. Composite figure A and composite figure B are similar. The length of the sides of composite figure A is two-thirds the length of the sides of composite figure B. If the area of composite figure A is 240 cm², find the area of composite figure B.

A
B
15 cm
22.5 cm
$A = 240$ cm²

11 Student Recording Sheet

Use this recording sheet with pages 816–817 of the Student Edition.

Multiple Choice

Read each question. Then fill in the correct answer.

1. Ⓐ Ⓑ Ⓒ Ⓓ   3. Ⓐ Ⓑ Ⓒ Ⓓ   5. Ⓐ Ⓑ Ⓒ Ⓓ

2. Ⓕ Ⓖ Ⓗ Ⓙ   4. Ⓕ Ⓖ Ⓗ Ⓙ

Short Response/Gridded Response

Record your answer in the blank.

For gridded response questions, also enter your answer in the grid by writing each number or symbol in a box. Then fill in the corresponding circle for that number or symbol.

6. _____ (grid in)

7. _____

8. _____

9. _____

10. _____ (grid in)

11. _____ (grid in)

6.

10.

11.

Extended Response

Record your answers for Question 12 on the back of this paper.

11   Rubric for Scoring Extended-Response

General Scoring Guidelines

- If a student gives only a correct numerical answer to a problem but does not show how he or she arrived at the answer, the student will be awarded only 1 credit. All extended-response questions require the student to show work.

- A fully correct answer for a multiple-part question requires correct responses for all parts of the question. For example, if a question has three parts, the correct response to one or two parts of the question that required work to be shown is *not* considered a fully correct response.

- Students who use trial and error to solve a problem must show their method. Merely showing that the answer checks or is correct is not considered a complete response for full credit.

Exercise 12 Rubric

Score	Specific Criteria
4	The student provides the correct areas of each figure and the appropriate total area. A well thought-out accurate explanation of how the areas model the Pythagorean Theorem is provided.
3	A generally correct solution, but may contain minor flaws in reasoning or computation.
2	A partially correct interpretation and/or solution to the problem.
1	A correct solution with no supporting evidence or explanation.
0	An incorrect solution indicating no mathematical understanding of the concept or task, or no solution is given.

11 Chapter 11 Quiz 1

(Lessons 11-1 and 11-2)

SCORE _____

Find the area of each figure. Round to the nearest tenth.

1.

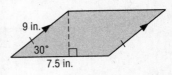

2.

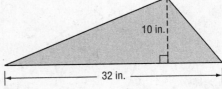

1. _____

3.

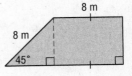

4.

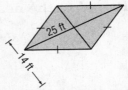

2. _____

3. _____

4. _____

5. The height of a triangle is 10 centimeters more than its base. If the area of the triangle is 100 square centimeters, find its base and height.

5. _____

- -

11 Chapter 11 Quiz 2

(Lesson 11-3)

SCORE _____

Find the area of each circle. Round to the nearest tenth.

1.

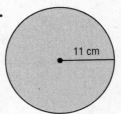

2.

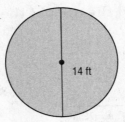

1. _____

2. _____

Find the area of each sector. Round to the nearest tenth.

3.

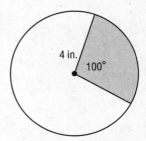

4.

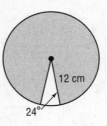

3. _____

4. _____

5. The area of a circle is 25 square feet. Find the diameter.

5. _____

11   Chapter 11 Quiz 3

(Lesson 11-4)

Find the area of each regular polygon. Round to the nearest tenth.

1.

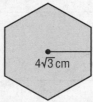

$4\sqrt{3}$ cm

2.

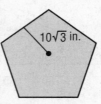

$10\sqrt{3}$ in.

1. _____

2. _____

Find the area of each figure. Round to the nearest tenth if necessary.

3.

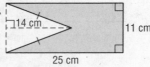

14 cm   11 cm

25 cm

4.

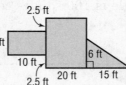

7 in.

4 in.

3. _____

4. _____

5. LAWN Leila has to buy grass seed for her lawn. Her lawn is in the composite figure shown. What is the area of the lawn? Round to the nearest tenth.

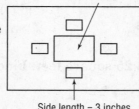

2.5 ft

5 ft

10 ft

2.5 ft

20 ft   6 ft   15 ft

5. _____

- -

11   Chapter 11 Quiz 4

(Lesson 11-5)

For each pair of similar figures, find the area of the shaded figure.

1.

7.5 m   12 m

$A = 720$ m²

2.

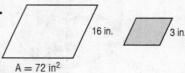

16 in.   3 in.

$A = 72$ in²

1. _____

2. _____

Find the value of *x*. Round to the nearest tenth.

3.

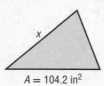

12 in.   *x*

$A = 88$ in² $A = 104.2$ in²

4.

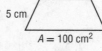

5 cm   *x*

$A = 100$ cm² $A = 40$ cm²

3. _____

4. _____

5. QUILT A quilt design has one large rectangle surrounded by four congruent rectangles, similar to the large rectangle. If the large rectangle has an area of 45 square inches, what is the area of each small rectangle?

Side length = 9 inches
Area = 45 in²

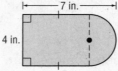

Side length = 3 inches

5. _____

11   Chapter 11 Mid-Chapter Test

(Lessons 11-1 through 11-3)

Part I   *Write the letter for the correct answer in the blank at the right of each question.*

1. Find the area of parallelogram *ABCD*. Round to the nearest tenth.

   A 145.5 cm²

   B 168.0 cm²

   C 190.5 cm²

   D 291.0 cm²

   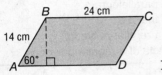

   1. _____

2. A right triangle has legs of length 10 feet and 13 feet. What is the area of the triangle?

   F 65 ft²

   G 100 ft²

   H 130 ft²

   J 150 ft²

   2. _____

3. Find the area of kite *ABCD*.

   A 22 cm²

   B 36 cm²

   C 72 cm²

   D 386 cm²

   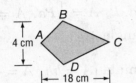

   3. _____

4. A trapezoid has base lengths of 2.5 inches and 10 inches and an altitude of 8 inches. What is the area of the trapezoid?

   F 25 in²

   G 50 in²

   H 100 in²

   J 200 in²

   4. _____

Part II

5. Find the area of the circle. Round to the nearest tenth.

   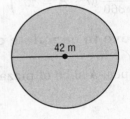

   5. _____

6. Find the area of rhombus *PQRS*. Round to the nearest tenth if necessary.

   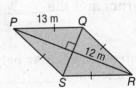

   6. _____

7. A sector of a circle has a central angle of 80°. If the circle has a radius of 5.5 inches, what is the area of the sector?

   7. _____

8. A trapezoid has base lengths of 4 and 19 feet, with an area of 115 square feet. What is the height of the trapezoid?

   8. _____

9. Find the radius of a circle with area of 615.8 square inches.

   9. _____

11 Chapter 11 Vocabulary Test

SCORE _____

apothem of a polygon	height of a parallelogram
base of a parallelogram	height of a trapezoid
base of a triangle	height of a triangle
center of a regular polygon	radius of a regular polygon
central angle of a regular polygon	sector of a circle

Select the correct formula to complete each sentence.

1. The area of a circle can be found by $\left(A = \frac{1}{2}Pa, \ A = \pi r^2, A = bh\right)$.

1. _____

2. $\left(A = \frac{1}{2}d_1d_2, \ A = \frac{1}{2}Pa, \ A = \frac{1}{2}bh\right)$ can be used to find the area of a triangle.

2. _____

3. The formula $\left(A = bh, \ A = \frac{1}{2}d_1d_2, \ A = \frac{1}{2}h(b_1 + b_2)\right)$ is used to find the area of a trapezoid.

3. _____

4. The area of all regular polygons can be found using $\left(A = \frac{1}{2}Pa, \ A = \frac{1}{2}d_1d_2, \ A = \frac{1}{2}bh\right)$.

4. _____

5. The formula to find the area of a sector is $\left(A = \frac{N}{360}\pi r^2 - \frac{1}{2}bh, \ A = \frac{N}{360}\pi r^2, \ A = \pi r^2\right)$.

5. _____

Choose from the terms above to complete each sentence.

6. In terms of geometric shapes, a slice of pizza closely resembles a____?____.

6. _____

7. The height of a parallelogram and the ____?____ are always perpendicular.

7. _____

8. A line drawn from the center of a regular polygon perpendicular to a side of the polygon is called a(n) ____?____.

8. _____

Define each term in your own words.

9. apothem

9. _____

10. height of a trapezoid

10. _____

11 Chapter 11 Test, Form 1

SCORE _____

Write the letter for the correct answer in the blank at the right of each question.

1. Find the area of parallelogram *ABCD*.
Round to the nearest tenth.

A 17.5 ft²   **C** 35 ft²

B 31.25 ft²   **D** 62.5 ft²

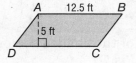

1. _____

2. Find the area of parallelogram *WXYZ*.
Round to the nearest tenth.

F 27.0 in²   **H** 63.6 in²

G 45.0 in²   **J** 81.0 in²

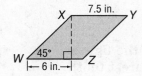

2. _____

3. Find the area of the trapezoid.
Round to the nearest tenth.

A 83.8 ft²   **C** 40.4 ft²

B 28.4 ft²   **D** 8.4 ft²

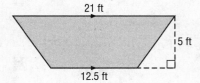

3. _____

4. Find the area of the kite.
Round to the nearest tenth.

F 38.0 mm²   **H** 9.5 mm²

G 19.0 mm²   **J** 5.0 mm²

4. _____

5. Find the area of the rhombus.
Round to the nearest tenth.

A 224.0 ft²   **C** 56.0 ft²

B 112.0 ft²   **D** 42.4 ft²

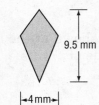

5. _____

6. The height of a parallelogram is 6 feet more than its base. If the area of
the parallelogram is 160 square feet, find the length of its base.

F 5 ft   **H** 6 ft

G 11 ft   **J** 10 ft

6. _____

7. Find the area of a regular octagon with a perimeter of 96 centimeters.

A about 695.3 cm²   **C** about 532 cm²

B about 576 cm²   **D** about 119.3 cm²

7. _____

8. Find the area of an equilateral triangle with a side length of 14 inches.

F about 12.1 in²   **H** about 84.9 in²

G about 42 in²   **J** about 254.6 in²

8. _____

11 Chapter 11 Test, Form 1 *(continued)*

9. Find the area of a circle with a circumference of 20π units.
   - **A** 400π units
   - **B** 314π units
   - **C** 200π units
   - **D** 100π units

   9. _____

10. What is the area of the shaded sector if the measure of ∠ABC is 70°?
    - **F** 15.3 in²
    - **G** 63.3 in²
    - **H** 381.8 in²
    - **J** 1581.7 in²

    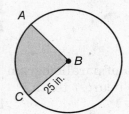

    10. _____

11. Find the area of the figure. Round to the nearest tenth.
    - **A** 23.4 ft²
    - **B** 28.3 ft²
    - **C** 29.7 ft²
    - **D** 36.0 ft²

    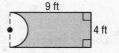

    11. _____

12. Find the area of quadrilateral *DEFG*.
    - **F** 154 cm²
    - **G** 218 cm²
    - **H** 244 cm²
    - **J** 308 cm²

    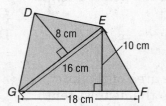

    12. _____

13. If the triangles shown at the right are similar, what is the value of *x*?
    - **A** 5 in.
    - **B** 16.8 in.
    - **C** 20.4 in.
    - **D** 30.8 in.

    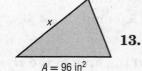

    10 in.

    A = 34 in²   *A* = 96 in²

    13. _____

14. Jim uses a small card and a large card that are similar in size in his magic show. What is the area of the small card?
    - **F** 42.7 in²
    - **G** 128.7 in²
    - **H** 84.7 in²
    - **J** 196.7 in²

    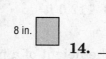

    24 in.

    8 in.

    A = 384 in²

    14. _____

15. Serena is wearing a pendant that was made by inscribing a square ruby in a sterling silver circle. The distance from the center of the pendant to its edge is 5.3 centimeters. Find the area of the pendant that is not covered by the ruby. Round to the nearest hundredth.
    - **A** 32.07 cm²   **B** 56.18 cm²   **C** 60.19 cm²   **D** 88.24 cm²

    15. _____

Bonus Find the area of the shaded segments.

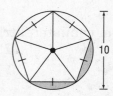

10

B: _____

11 **Chapter 11 Test, Form 2A**

Write the letter for the correct answer in the blank at the right of each question.

1. Find the area of parallelogram *ABCD*.
   Round to the nearest tenth.

   A 55.4 m²   **C** 69.3 m²

   B 60 m²   **D** 80 m²

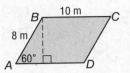

   1. _____

2. The area of the parallelogram DEFG is 143 square units.
   Find the height. Round to the nearest tenth.

   F 11 units   **H** 22 units

   G 14.3 units   **J** 44 units

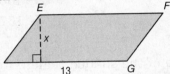

   2. _____

3. The base of a triangle is three times its height.
   If the area of a triangle is 54 square inches, find its height.

   A 18 in.   **C** 3 in.

   B 6 in.   **D** 1 in.

   3. _____

4. Find the area of quadrilateral *PQRS*.

   F 34.1 units²   **H** 130 units²

   G 65 units²   **J** 360 units²

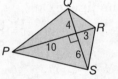

   4. _____

5. A trapezoid has a height of 3 meters, a base length of 8 meters, and
   an area of 30 square meters. What is the length of the other base?

   A 12 m   **C** 19 m

   B 11 m   **D** 24 m

   5. _____

6. Rhombus *ABCD* has an area of 264 square units.
   If *DB* = 12 units, find *AC*.

   F 44 units   **H** 18 units

   G 22 units   **J** 12 units

   6. _____

7. The area of a circle is 314.2 square feet. What is the length of its radius?

   A 10 ft   **C** 31.4 ft

   B 20 ft   **D** 62.8 ft

   7. _____

8. If *m∠ACB* = 36, find the area of the shaded sector.

   F 7.9 in²   **H** 25 in²

   G 22.5 in²   **J** 70.7 in²

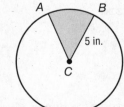

   8. _____

9. Find the area of a regular hexagon with side length of 10 centimeters. Round to the nearest tenth.

    A 129.9 cm²   **C** 259.8 cm²

    B 150 cm²   **D** 519.6 cm²

                                                    9. _____

10. Find the area of a regular nonagon with a perimeter of 126 inches. Round to the nearest tenth.

    F 1289.4 in²   **H** 466.2 in²

    G 1211.6 in²   **J** 157.5 in²

                                                   10. _____

11. Find the area of the shaded region. Round to the nearest tenth.

    A 59.1 cm²   **C** 25.7 cm²

    B 57.5 cm²   **D** 19.6 cm²

                                                   11. _____

12. Find the area of the figure.

    F 31 ft²   **H** 60 ft²

    G 40 ft²   **J** 80 ft²

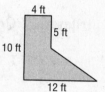

                                                   12. _____

13. A running track consists of two parallel lines that are connected at each end by the curved boundary of a semicircle. The parallel lines are 30 meters long and 7 meters apart. Find the area inside the running track.

    A 229.24 m²   **C** 312.46 m²

    B 248.48 m²   **D** 363.93 m²

                                                   13. _____

14. Find the area of the regular octagon.

    F 8.5 mm²   **H** 237 mm²

    G 119 mm²   **J** 476 mm²

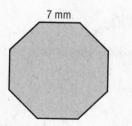

                                                   14. _____

15. A circular pizza has a diameter of 16 inches. Each slice of pizza has a central angle of 45°. What is the area of each slice of pizza ?

    A 3.1 in²

    B 6.3 in³   **C** 25.1 in²

                     D 100.5 in²

                                                    15. _____

Bonus Find the area of a circle circumscribed about a regular pentagon with a perimeter of 50 inches. Round to the nearest tenth.   **B:** _____

11   Chapter 11 Test, Form 2B

Assessment

Write the letter for the correct answer in the blank at the right of each question.

1. Find the area of parallelogram *ABCD*.
Round to the nearest tenth.
  A 54 in²   **C** 95.2 in²
  B 76.4 in²   **D** 152.7 in²

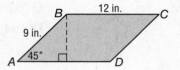

1. _____

2. The area of parallelogram *PQRS* is 187 square units.
Find the base *x* if the height is 11 units.
  F 14 units   **H** 27 units
  G 8.5 units   **J** 17 units

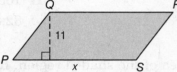

2. _____

3. The height of a parallelogram is one-third its base. If the area of the
parallelogram is 363 square inches, find its base and height.
  A $b = 33$ in.; $h = 11$ in.   **C** $b = 11$ in.; $h = 33$ in.
  B $b = 121$ in., $h = 2$ in.   **D** $b = 30$ in.; $h = 33$ in.

3. _____

4. Find the area of kite *ABCD*.
  F 10.5 cm²   **H** 52 cm²
  G 21 cm²   **J** 104 cm²

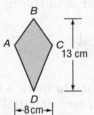

4. _____

5. A trapezoid has base lengths of 8.5 and 14.5 feet with an
area of 184 square feet. What is the height of the trapezoid?
  A 4 ft   **C** 16 ft
  B 8 ft   **D** 23 ft

5. _____

6. Rhombus *ABCD* has an area of 126 square units.
If *DB* = 18 units, find *AC*.
  F 18 units   **H** 7 units
  G 14 units   **J** 3.5 units

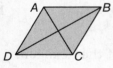

6. _____

7. Find the diameter of a circle with an area of 804.2 square centimeters.
  A 8 cm   **C** 48 cm
  B 32 cm   **D** 64 cm

7. _____

8. If $m\overset{\frown}{EGF} = 235$, find the area of the shaded sector.
  F 82.3 in²   **H** 436.3 in²
  G 820.3 in²   **J** 1256.6 in²

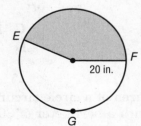

8. _____

9. Find the area of an equilateral triangle with a side length of
   12 centimeters. Round to the nearest tenth if necessary.
   A 187.1 cm²   **C** 62.4 cm²
   B 93.5 cm²   **D** 54 cm²   9. _____

10. Find the area of a regular octagon with a perimeter of 80 inches. Round to
    the nearest tenth.
    F 965.7 in²   **H** 165.7 in²
    G 482.8 in²   **J** 82.8 in²   10. _____

11. Find the area of the shaded region. Round to the
    nearest tenth.
    A 12.6 m²   **C** 32.9 m²
    B 24.6 m²   **D** 44.9 m²   11. _____

12. Find the area of the figure. Round to the nearest tenth.
    F 14.6 units²   **H** 18.2 units²
    G 15.0 units²   **J** 22.4 units²   12. _____

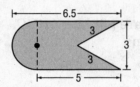

13. Gerry wants to have a cover made for his swimming pool which
    consists of two parallel lines that are connected at each end by the
    curved boundary of a semicircle. The parallel lines are 12 feet long
    and 10 feet apart. Find the area of the swimming pool cover.
    A 572.39 ft²   **C** 434.16 ft²
    B 233.02 ft²   **D** 198.54 ft²   13. _____

14. Find the area of the hexagon.
    F 69.9 ft²   **H** 279.4 ft²
    G 419.2 ft²   **J** 634.7 ft²   14.. _____

15. A pie has a diameter of 9 inches. Each slice of
    the pie has a central angle of 45°. What is the area of each
    slice of pie?
    A 8.0 in²   **C** 127.2 in²
    B 31.8 in²   **D** 221.8 in²   15. _____

Bonus Find the area of a circle circumscribed about a regular
       octagon with a perimeter of 80 inches. Round to the
       nearest tenth.   **B:** _____

11 Chapter 11 Test, Form 2C

SCORE _____

For Question 1 and 2, find the area of each parallelogram. Round to the nearest tenth if neccessary.

1.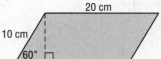

2.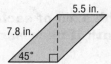

1. _____

2. _____

3. The area of parallelogram *ABCD* is 2250 square meters. What is the height of the parallelogram?

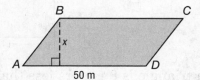

3. _____

4. Find the area of the trapezoid.

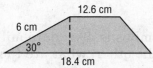

4. _____

5. Find the area of the kite.

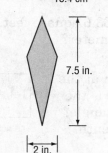

5. _____

6. Find the area of the triangle.

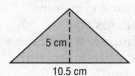

6. _____

7. Find the area of the rhombus. If *XY* = 8 feet and *XA* = 5 feet.

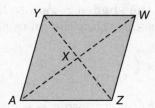

7. _____

8. Find the area of a square with side length $4\sqrt{2}$ inches. Round to the nearest tenth.

8. _____

9. Find the area of a regular hexagon with an apothem length of 4.3 centimeters. Round to the nearest tenth.

9. _____

10. Jamie shades in a piece of a circle defined by a central angle of 12°. Find the area of the shaded sector.

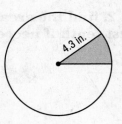

10. _____

For Questions 11 and 12, find the area of each figure. Round to the nearest tenth if necessary.

11.

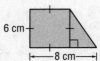

6 cm
8 cm

12.

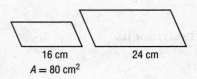

6.6 m
14.3 m

11. _____

12. _____

13. The height of a triangle is 8 meters less than its base. If the area of the triangle is 212.5 square meters, find the length of its base and height.

13. _____

14. The area of a rhombus is 49 square millimeters. If one diagonal is twice as long as the other, what are the lengths of the diagonals?

14. _____

15. The area of a circle is 63.6 square feet. To the nearest tenth, what is the length of the diameter?

15. _____

16. If the rectangles shown at the right are similar, what is the area of the shaded rectangle? Round to the nearest tenth.

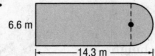

20 m
15 m
$A = 500\ m^2$

16. _____

17. Carlos cuts blue parallelograms and larger red parallelograms to use in his decoupage. He realizes the parallelograms are similar. What is the area of the larger, red parallelogram? Round to the nearest tenth.

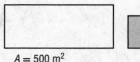

16 cm   24 cm
$A = 80\ cm^2$

17. _____

18. Find the area of the shaded region to the nearest tenth. Assume that the triangle is equilateral.

10 in.

18. _____

Bonus If the height of a trapezoid is 4 meters, the length of one of its bases is 11 meters, and its area is 62 square meters, what is the measure of the other base?

B: _____

11   Chapter 11 Test, Form 2D

For Question 1 and 2, find the area of each parallelogram. Round to the nearest tenth if neccessary.

1.

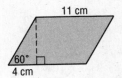

11 cm
60°
4 cm

2.

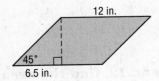

12 in.
45°
6.5 in.

1. _____

2. _____

3. If the area of parallelogram *ABCD* is 570 square meters, find the height.

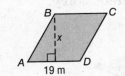

B   C
x
A   D
19 m

3. _____

4. Find the area of the trapezoid.

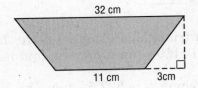

32 cm
11 cm   3cm

4. _____

5. Find the area of the kite.

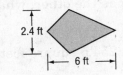

2.4 ft
6 ft

5. _____

6. Find the area of the triangle.

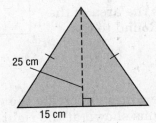

25 cm
15 cm

6. _____

7. Find the area of the rhombus.

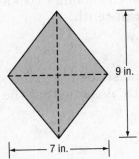

9 in.
7 in.

7. _____

8. Find the area of a square with apothem length of 3 inches. Round to the nearest tenth.

8. _____

9. Find the area of a regular hexagon with a side length of 15 centimeters. Round to the nearest tenth.

9. _____

11 · Chapter 11 Test, Form 2D *(continued)*

10. If $m\widehat{AB} = 105$, find the area of the shaded sector. Round to the nearest tenth.

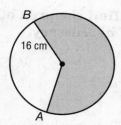

10. _____

For Questions 11 and 12, find the area of each figure. Round to the nearest tenth if necessary.

11.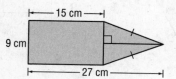

12.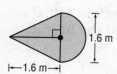

11. _____

12. _____

13. The height of a triangle is 4 meters more than its base. If the area of the triangle is 160 square meters, find its base and height.

13. _____

14. The area of a rhombus is 337.5 square millimeters. If one diagonal is three times as long as the other, what are the lengths of the diagonals?

14. _____

15. The area of a circle is 254.5 square feet, what is the diameter?

15. _____

16. If the rectangles shown at the right are similar, what is the area of the shaded rectangle? Round to the nearest tenth.

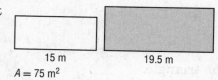

15 m   19.5 m
$A = 75\ m^2$

16. _____

17. Ben uses two cookie cutters to create the similar parallelograms shown at the right. What is the area of the smaller cookie? Round to the nearest tenth.

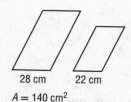

28 cm   22 cm
$A = 140\ cm^2$

17. _____

18. Find the area of the shaded region to the nearest tenth. Assume that the hexagon is regular.

8 in.

18. _____

Bonus If one diagonal of a rhombus is 15 meters long and its area is 157.5 square meters, find the measures of the other diagonal?   B: _____

SCORE _____

11 **Chapter 11 Test, Form 3**

For Question 1 and 2, find the area of each parallelogram. Round to the nearest tenth if neccessary.

1.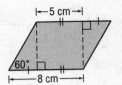

2.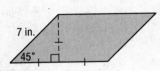

1. _____

2. _____

3. _____

3. Find the area of the figure.

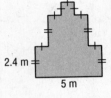

For Questions 4–10, find the area of each figure. Round to the nearest tenth if necessary.

4. the trapezoid at the right

4. _____

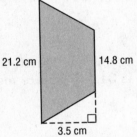
21.2 cm   14.8 cm
3.5 cm

5. the kite at the right if the value of x is 4.9

5. _____

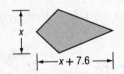
x $x + 7.6$

6. the triangle at the right

6. _____

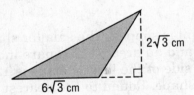
$2\sqrt{3}$ cm
$6\sqrt{3}$ cm

7. a rhombus with a perimeter of 100 meters and one diagonal with a length of 48 meters

7. _____

8. a regular octagon with perimeter of 96 meters

8. _____

9. a regular pentagon with apothem length of 5 inches

9. _____

10. the shaded sector of the circle at the right

10. _____

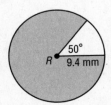
50°
R 9.4 mm

For Questions 11–13, find the area of each figure. Round to the nearest tenth if necessary.

11.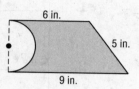

12.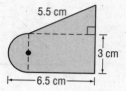

11. _____

12. _____

13.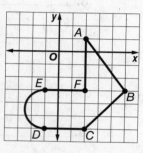

13. _____

14. The height of a triangle is one-fourth the length of its base. If the area of the triangle is 34.445 square meters, find the length of its base and height.

14. _____

15. The area of a rhombus is 1156 square millimeters. If one diagonal is half as long as the other, what are the lengths of the diagonals?

15. _____

16. The area of a circle is 2.01 square feet. What is the diameter?

16. _____

17. Jillian has two similar shapes. The smaller shape has a side length of 5 inches and an area of 17 square inches. The length of the corresponding side of the larger shape is 12 inches. Find the area of the larger shape. Round to the nearest tenth.

17. _____

Bonus Find the area of the shaded region to the nearest tenth. Assume that the hexagon is regular

B: _____

11 Extended-Response Test

Demonstrate your knowledge by giving a clear, concise solution to each problem. Be sure to include all relevant drawings and justify your answers. You may show your solution in more than one way or investigate beyond the requirements of the problem.

1. a. Explain how a 30°-60°-90° triangle is used in finding the area of parallelogram *PQRS*.

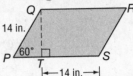

b. Find the area of parallelogram *PQRS* to the nearest tenth.

2. Explain how to find the area of each figure described below, then find each area. Round to the nearest tenth if necessary.

a.

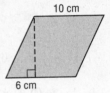

b.

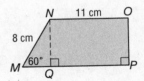

c. the shaded region

3. Describe the dimensions of a similar trapezoid that has an area four times the area of the one shown. Explain how you found your answer.

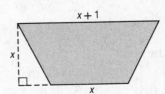

11 Standardized Test Practice

SCORE _____

(Chapters 1–11)

Part 1: Multiple Choice

Instructions: Fill in the appropriate circle for the best answer.

---

1. Mai knows that if two arcs are congruent, then their corresponding central angles are congruent. She is given $\odot D$ with $\overset{\frown}{BC} \cong \overset{\frown}{GH}$, and she concludes that $\angle BDC \cong \angle GDH$. Which form of reasoning does she use? (Lesson 2-4)

  A Inductive Reasoning   **C** Law of Syllogism
  B Law of Detachment   **D** Formal Proof

1. Ⓐ Ⓑ Ⓒ Ⓓ

2. The distance between A and B is 17.8 centimeters, and the distance between B and C is 9.5 centimeters. If A, B, and C are noncollinear, which inequality represents the possible distance between A and C? (Lesson 5-3)

  F $9.5 \text{ cm} < AC < 17.8 \text{ cm}$ **H** $10 \text{ cm} < AC < 18 \text{ cm}$
  G $8.3 \text{ cm} < AC < 27.3 \text{ cm}$ **J** $8 \text{ cm} < AC < 27 \text{ cm}$

2. Ⓕ Ⓖ Ⓗ Ⓙ

3. Find HK. (Lesson 8-3)

  A $3\sqrt{2}$ **C** $6\sqrt{2}$
  B 6 **D** $2\sqrt{3}$

3. Ⓐ Ⓑ Ⓒ Ⓓ

4. Which expression can you use to find a? (Lesson 7-4)

  F $c^2 - b^2$ **H** $\dfrac{b+c}{2}$
  G $2b - c$ **J** $2c - b$

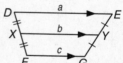

4. Ⓕ Ⓖ Ⓗ Ⓙ

5. If $\overline{ST}$ with endpoints $S(3, -7)$ and $T(-5, -2)$ is reflected in the line $y = x$, find the coordinates of $\overline{S'T'}$. (Lesson 9-1)

  A $S'(-3, -7)$ and $T'(5, -2)$ **C** $S'(-3, 7)$ and $T'(5, 2)$
  B $S'(3, 7)$ and $T'(-5, 2)$ **D** $S'(-7, 3)$ and $T'(-2, -5)$

5. Ⓐ Ⓑ Ⓒ Ⓓ

6. Find the circumference of a circle with a radius of 26.5 centimeters. (Lesson 10-1)

  F 26.5π cm   **G** 53π cm   **H** 702.25π cm   **J** 2809π cm

6. Ⓕ Ⓖ Ⓗ Ⓙ

7. Find $m\angle 1$. (Lesson 10-6)

  A 61   **C** 82
  B 98   **D** 103

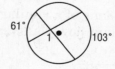

7. Ⓐ Ⓑ Ⓒ Ⓓ

8. Find the area of a regular hexagon with a perimeter of 72 inches. Round to the nearest square inch. (Lesson 11-3)

  F 72 in^2 **G** 432 in^2 **H** 374 in^2 **J** 864 in^2

8. Ⓕ Ⓖ Ⓗ Ⓙ

11 Standardized Test Practice (continued)

9. If $LM = 3x + 2$, $MN = 7x - 18$, and $NL = 22 - x$, find the length of the sides of equilateral triangle LMN. (Lesson 4-1)

   A 5   **B** 10   **C** 12   **D** 17   **9.** Ⓐ Ⓑ Ⓒ Ⓓ

10. Find x. (Lesson 8-3)

   F $\dfrac{4}{\sqrt{4}}$ **H** $4\sqrt{2}$

   G 4   **J** $8\sqrt{2}$ **10.** Ⓕ Ⓖ Ⓗ Ⓙ

11. Find x to the nearest hundredth. (Lesson 8-6)

   A 4.70   **C** 13.82

   B 12.77   **D** 21.17   **11.** Ⓐ Ⓑ Ⓒ Ⓓ

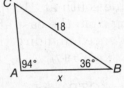

12. The diameter of a circle is 34 inches, and a chord of the circle 18 inches. Find the distance between the chord and the center of the circle to the nearest tenth. (Lesson 10-3)

   F 14.4 in.   **G** 15.6 in.   **H** 17.3 in.   **J** 19.23 in.   **12.** Ⓕ Ⓖ Ⓗ Ⓙ

Part 2: Gridded Response

Instructions: Enter your answer by writing each digit of the answer in a column box and then shading in the appropriate circle that corresponds to that entry.

13. Angles B and G are opposite angles of a parallelogram. Find $m\angle G$ if $m\angle B = 3x + 80$ and $m\angle G = 140 - x$. (Lesson 6-2)

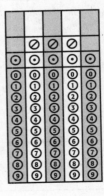

14. The rectangles shown are similar. What is the area of the smaller rectangle? (Lesson 11-5)

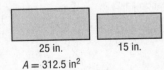

    25 in.   15 in.

    $A = 312.5$ in²

11 **Standardized Test Practice** *(continued)*

Part 3: Short Response

Instructions: Write your answer in the space provided.

15. Find the values of *a* and *b* to the nearest tenth. (Lesson 8-6)

15. _____

16. If *ABCD* is a parallelogram, find $m\angle DAB$, $m\angle CDA$, and *x*. (Lesson 6-2)

16. _____

17. A plane is flying due south at 310 miles per hour and the wind is blowing from the east at 40 miles per hour. Find the resultant speed and direction of the plane to the nearest tenth. (Lesson 8-7)

17. _____

18. Find $m\angle R$, $m\angle S$, $m\angle QTR$, and $m\angle QTS$ if $\widehat{SR} \cong \widehat{TS}$. (Lesson 10-4)

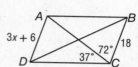

18. _____

19. If $\triangle XYZ$ with vertices $X(0, 3)$, $Y(4, 7)$, and $Z(-5, 4)$ is reflected in the *x*-axis and then the *y*-axis, find the coordinates of the rotated image. (Lesson 9-4)

19. _____

20. Find $m\angle TRU$, $m\angle URV$, and $m\angle VRW$. (Lesson 10-2)

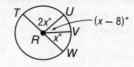

20. _____

21. Trapezoid *STWX* has an area of 517.5 square inches. Find the height of *STWX*. (Lesson 11-2)

21. _____

22. Given the regular polygon *ABCDEF*:

   a. Find the sum of the measures of the interior angles of *ABCDEF*. (Lesson 6-1)

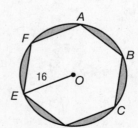

22 a. _____

   b. Find the area of the shaded region. Round to the nearest tenth. (Lesson 11-3)

b. _____

Answers (Anticipation Guide and Lesson 11-1)

11-1 Study Guide and Intervention

Areas of Parallelograms and Triangles

Areas of Parallelograms Any side of a parallelogram can be called a **base**. The height of a parallelogram is the perpendicular distance between any two parallel bases. The area of a parallelogram is the product of the base and the height.

Area of a Parallelogram	If a parallelogram has an area of A square units, a base of b units, and a height of h units, then $A = bh$.

Example Find the area of parallelogram $EFGH$.

$A = bh$ Area of a parallelogram
$= 30(18)$ $b = 30$, $h = 18$
$= 540$ Multiply.

The area is 540 square meters.

Exercises

Find the perimeter and area of each parallelogram. Round to the nearest tenth if necessary.

1. 71.8 ft; 288 ft²

2. 96 in.; 498.8 in²

3. 6.4 cm; 2.56 cm²

4. 60 in.; 160 in²

5. 90 ft; 318.2 ft²

6. 16.4 cm; 16.8 cm²

7. **TILE FLOOR** A bathroom tile floor is made of black-and-white parallelograms. Each parallelogram is made of two triangles with dimensions as shown. Find the perimeter and area of one parallelogram.

36 cm; 73.7 cm²

---

11 Anticipation Guide

Areas of Polygons and Circles

Step 1

- Read each statement.
- Decide whether you Agree (A) or Disagree (D) with the statement.
- Write A or D in the first column OR if you are not sure whether you agree or disagree, write NS (Not Sure).

Before you begin Chapter 11

STEP 1 A, D, or NS	Statement	STEP 2 A or D
	1. The area of a parallelogram whose sides measure 5 cm and 9 cm is 5 cm × 9 cm or 45 cm².	D
	2. The area of a triangle is one-half its base times its height.	A
	3. The area of a kite is the product of its diagonals.	D
	4. The area of a rhombus equals half the product of the lengths of its diagonals.	A
	5. A segment drawn from the center to a vertex of a regular polygon is called an apothem.	D
	6. The formula for the area of a circle is $A = \pi r^2$.	A
	7. The area of an irregular figure can be found by separating the figure into shapes with known area formulas.	A
	8. If an irregular figure is in the shape of a pentagon, then the formula for the area of a regular pentagon can be used to find its area.	D
	9. A sector of a circle with a central angle of 35° will have an area of $\frac{35}{360} \cdot \pi r^2$.	A
	10. If two polygons are similar, then their areas are proportional to the square of the scale factor between them.	A

Step 2 *After you complete Chapter 11*

- Reread each statement and complete the last column by entering an A or a D.
- Did any of your opinions about the statements change from the first column?
- For those statements that you mark with a D, use a piece of paper to write an example of why you disagree.

Answers

Answers (Lesson 11-1)

11-1 Skills Practice

Areas of Parallelograms and Triangles

Find the perimeter and area of each parallelogram or triangle. Round to the nearest tenth if necessary.

1.

64.1 mm; 108 mm²

2.

19 ft, 19.1 ft²

3.

42 yd; 69.3 yd²

4.

96 in., 404.5 in²

5.

13.6 m; 11.6 m²

6.

55 km; 166.5 km²

7.

100 cm; 519.6 cm²

8.

58 in; 144.5 in²

9. The height of a parallelogram is 10 feet more than its base. If the area of the parallelogram is 1200 square feet, find its base and height.

b = 30 ft; h = 40 ft

10. The base of a triangle is one half of its height. If the area of the triangle is 196 square millimeters, find its base and height.

b = 14 mm; h = 28 mm

11-1 Study Guide and Intervention (continued)

Areas of Parallelograms and Triangles

Areas Of Triangles The area of a triangle is one half the product of the base and its corresponding height. Like a parallelogram, the base can be any side, and the height is the length of an altitude drawn to a given base.

Area of a Triangle	If a triangle has an area of A square units, a base of b units, and a corresponding height of h units, then $A = \frac{1}{2}bh$.

Example Find the area of the triangle.

Area of a triangle

$A = \frac{1}{2}bh$

$= \frac{1}{2}(24)(28)$ $b = 24, h = 28$

$= 336$ Multiply.

The area is 336 square meters.

Exercises

Find the perimeter and area of each triangle. Round to the nearest tenth if necessary.

1.

34.5 cm; 30 cm²

2.

73.9 ft; 176 ft²

3.

92.5 in.; 220 in²

4.

49.5 cm; 58.5 cm²

5.

75.6 in; 234 in²

6.

71.7 mm; 220.5 mm²

7. LOGO The logo for an engineering company is on a poster at a job fair. The logo consists of two triangles that have the dimensions shown. What are the perimeter and area of each triangle?

Triangle 1: 77 in.; 250 in²;
Triangle 2: 85.4 in.; 312.5 in²

NAME _____ DATE _____ PERIOD _____

11-1 | Practice

Areas of Parallelograms and Triangles

Find the perimeter and area of each parallelogram or triangle. Round to the nearest tenth if necessary.

1.
(5 m, 11 m, 60°)

32 m; 47.6 m²

2. (8 cm, 45°, 10 cm)

36 cm; 56.6 cm²

3. (10 in., 45°)

34.1 in.; 50 in²

4. (17 cm, 15 cm, 25 cm)

91.1 cm; 212.5 cm²

5. (12 in., 20 in., 16 in.)

55.3 in.; 120 in²

6. (4 ft, 12.8 ft, 8 ft, 6 ft)

26.8 ft; 16 ft²

7. The height of a parallelogram is 5 feet more than its base. If the area of the parallelogram is 204 square feet, find its base and height.

b = 12 ft, h = 17 ft

8. The height of a parallelogram is three times its base. If the area of the parallelogram is 972 square inches, find its base and height.

b = 18 in., h = 54 in.

9. The base of a triangle is four times its height. If the area of the triangle is 242 square millimeters, find its base and height.

b = 44 mm; h = 11 mm

10. FRAMING A rectangular poster measures 42 inches by 26 inches. A frame shop fitted the poster with a half-inch mat border.

a. Find the area of the poster. **1092 in²**

b. Find the area of the mat border. **69 in²**

c. Suppose the wall is marked where the poster will hang. The marked area includes an additional 12-inch space around the poster and frame. Find the total wall area that has been marked for the poster. **3417 in²**

NAME _____ DATE _____ PERIOD _____

11-1 | Word Problem Practice

Areas of Parallelograms and Triangles

1. PACKAGING A box with a square opening is squashed into the rhombus shown below.

(14 in., 7 in.)

What is the area of the opening? **98 in²**

2. RUNNING Jason jogs once around a city block shaped like a parallelogram.
(200 yd, 100 yd)

How far did Jason jog? **600 yd**

3. SHADOWS A rectangular billboard casts a shadow on the ground in the shape of a parallelogram. What is the area of the ground covered by the shadow? Round your answer to the nearest tenth.
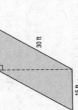
(15 ft, 30 ft)

389.7 ft²

4. PATHS A concrete path shown below is made by joining several parallelograms.
(102 in., 128 in., 48 in., 100 in., 48 in., 144 in., 106 in.)

What is the total area of the path? **58,548 in²**

5. HIGHWAY SUPPORTS Three columns are being placed at the vertices of a right triangle to support a highway. Two of the columns are marked on the coordinate plane shown.

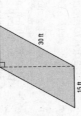

a. What are two possible locations of the third column to form a right triangle?

(−2, 4) or (−4, −2)

b. What is the area in square units of each of the two right triangles that result from the possibilities you found in part **a**? Explain.

6 square units; Each triangle is 2 units by 6 units.

NAME ______________ DATE ________ PERIOD ________

11-1 Enrichment

Area of a Parallelogram

You can prove some interesting results using the formula you have proved for the area of a parallelogram by drawing auxiliary lines to form congruent regions. Consider the top parallelogram shown at the right. In the figure, d is the length of the diagonal $\overline{BD}$, and k is the length of the perpendicular segment from A to $\overline{BD}$. Now consider the second figure, which shows the same parallelogram with a number of auxiliary perpendiculars added. Use what you know about perpendicular lines, parallel lines, and congruent triangles to answer the following.

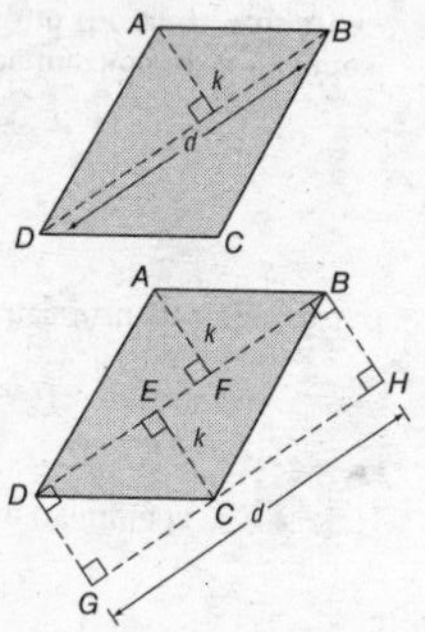

1. What kind of figure is $DBHG$?

rectangle

2. If you moved $\triangle AFB$ to the lower-left end of figure $DBHG$, would it fit perfectly on top of $\triangle DGC$? Explain your answer.

Yes; $\triangle AFB \cong \triangle CED$ (by HA) and $\triangle CED \cong \triangle DGC$ (Since $\overline{DC}$ is a diagonal of rectangle $DECD$). So $\triangle AFB \cong \triangle DGC$.

3. Which two triangular pieces of $\square ABCD$ are congruent to $\triangle CBH$?

$\triangle DAF$ and $\triangle BCE$

4. The area of $\square ABCD$ is the same as that of figure $DBHG$, since the pieces of $\square ABCD$ can be rearranged to form $DBHG$. Express the area of $\square ABCD$ in terms of the measurements k and d.

Area of $\square ABCD = dk$

Copyright © Glencoe/McGraw-Hill, a division of The McGraw-Hill Companies, Inc.

NAME ______________ DATE ________ PERIOD ________

11-1 Graphing Calculator Activity

Cabri Junior: Areas of Parallelograms

Cabri Junior can be used to find the perimeters and areas of parallelograms.

Step 1 Draw a parallelogram.

- Select **F2 Segment** to draw a segment.
- Select **F5 Alph-num** to label the endpoints of the segment A and B.
- Draw segment AD.
- Select **F3 Parallel** to draw a line parallel to segment AB through D. Select point D, and then segment AB.
- Draw a line parallel to segment AD through B.
- Select **F2 Point, Intersection** to place a point at the intersection of the two lines drawn. Label the point C.
- Select **F2 Quad** and draw a quadrilateral by selecting points A, B, C, and D.

Step 2 Find the measure of the area of parallelogram $ABCD$.

- Select **F5 Measure, Area.**
- Place the cursor on any segment of parallelogram $ABCD$. Then press ENTER.
- The area appears with the hand attached. Move the number to an appropriate place.

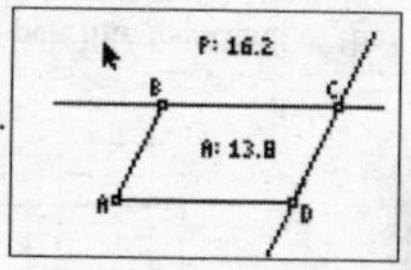

Step 3 Find the measure of the perimeter of parallelogram $ABCD$.

- Select **F5 Measure, D. & Length.**
- Place the cursor on any segment of parallelogram $ABCD$. Then press ENTER.
- The area appears with the hand attached. Move the number to an appropriate place.

The perimeter of the parallelogram shown here is 16.2 units and the area is 13.8 square units.

Exercises **See students' work.**

Analyze your drawing.

1. Find the lengths of all four sides of the parallelogram.
2. Using the information from Exercise 1, what is the perimeter of the parallelogram? Does this measurement match that found by Cabri Junior?
3. Construct a line segment showing the height of the parallelogram. What is the length of the line segment?
4. What is the measure of the base of the parallelogram?
5. Using the information from Exercises 3 and 4, what is the area of the parallelogram? Does this measurement match the one found by Cabri Junior?
6. Select one of the vertices and drag it to change the dimensions of the parallelogram. (Press CLEAR so the pointer becomes a black arrow. Move the pointer close to a vertex until the arrow becomes transparent and the vertex is blinking. Press ALPHA to change the arrow to a hand. Then move the vertex.) Do you see any patterns or relationships?

Copyright © Glencoe/McGraw-Hill, a division of The McGraw-Hill Companies, Inc.

Lesson 11-2

NAME _____ DATE _____ PERIOD _____

11-2 Study Guide and Intervention

Areas of Trapezoids, Rhombi, and Kites

Areas of Trapezoids A trapezoid is a quadrilateral with exactly one pair of parallel sides, called bases. The **height of a trapezoid** is the perpendicular distance between the bases. The area of a trapezoid is the product of one half the height and the sum of the lengths of the bases.

Area of a Trapezoid	If a trapezoid has an area of A square units, bases of b_1 and b_2 units, and a height of h units, then $A = \frac{1}{2}h(b_1 + b_2)$

Example Find the area of the trapezoid.

$A = \frac{1}{2}h(b_1 + b_2)$ Area of a trapezoid

$= \frac{1}{2}(15)(18 + 40)$ $h = 15$, $b_1 = 18$, and $b_2 = 40$

$= 435$ Simplify.

The area of the trapezoid is 435 square meters.

Exercises

Find the area of each trapezoid.

1.
400 ft²

2.
504 yd²

3.
820 m²

4.
57.5 in²

5.
177 cm²

6.
384 ft²

7. **OPEN ENDED** Ryan runs a landscaping business. A new customer has a trapezodial shaped backyard, shown at the right. How many square feet of grass will Ryan have to mow?
$975\frac{3}{8}$ ft²

Chapter 11   13   Glencoe Geometry

Lesson 11-1

NAME _____ DATE _____ PERIOD _____

11-1 Geometer's Sketchpad Activity

Areas of Parallelograms

The Geometer's Sketchpad can be used to find the perimeters and areas of parallelograms.

Step 1 Use The Geometer's Sketchpad to draw a parallelogram.
- Construct a segment by selecting the Segment tool from the toolbar. First, click the first point. Then click on a second point to draw the segment.
- Next, use one of the endpoints of the original segment as the first point for the new segment and click on a second point to construct the new segment.
- Construct a parallel line to the original segment by first highlighting the original segment and the endpoint not on that segment. Then select **Parallel Line** from the **Construct** menu.
- Construct a parallel line to the second segment by highlighting the second segment and the point not on it. Then select **Parallel Line** from the **Construct** menu.
- Next, construct a point on the intersection of the two lines. Use the Point tool from the toolbar to select the point where the two lines intersect.
- Construct the interior of the parallelogram by highlighting all four points and selecting **Quadrilateral Interior** under the **Construct** menu.

Step 2 Use The Geometer's Sketchpad to find the perimeter of the parallelogram.
- Highlight the interior of the parallelogram using the Selection Arrow tool from the toolbar.
- Next, find the perimeter by selecting **Perimeter** under the **Measure** menu.

Step 3 Use The Geometer's Sketchpad to find the area of the parallelogram.
- Highlight the interior of the parallelogram using the Selection Arrow tool from the toolbar.
- Next, find the area by selecting **Area** under the **Measure** menu.

The perimeter of the parallelogram shown here is 11.33 cm and the area is 6.63 cm².

Exercises   See students' work.

Analyze your drawing.

1. Find the lengths of all four sides of the parallelogram.

2. Using the information from Exercise 1, what is the perimeter of the parallelogram? Does this measurement match that found by the Geometer's Sketchpad?

3. Construct a line segment showing the height of the parallelogram. What is the length of the line segment?

4. What is the measure of the base of the parallelogram?

5. Using the information from Exercises 3 and 4, what is the area of the parallelogram? Does this measurement match the one found by the Geometer's Sketchpad?

6. Select one of the vertices and drag it to change the dimensions of the parallelogram. Do you see any patterns or relationships?

Chapter 11   12   Glencoe Geometry

11-2 Skills Practice

Areas of Trapezoids, Rhombi, and Kites

Find the area of each trapezoid, rhombus, or kite.

1.

105 m²

2.

84 mm²

3.

123.75 in²

4.

80 ft²

5.

32 m²

6.

447.75 cm²

ALGEBRA Find each missing length.

7. A trapezoid has base lengths of 6 and 15 centimeters with an area of 136.5 square centimeters. What is the height of the trapezoid?

13 cm

8. One diagonal of a kite is four times as long as the other diagonal. If the area of the kite is 72 square meters, what are the lengths of the diagonals?

6 m; 24 m

9. A trapezoid has a height of 24 meters, a base of 4 meters, and an area of 264 square meters. What is the length of the other base?

18 m

Chapter 11   15   *Glencoe Geometry*

11-2 Study Guide and Intervention (continued)

Areas of Trapezoids, Rhombi, and Kites

Areas of Rhombi and Kites A rhombus is a parallelogram with all four sides congruent. A kite is a quadrilateral with exactly two pairs of consecutive sides congruent.

Area of Rhombus or Kite	If a rhombus or kite has an area of A square units, and diagonals of d_1 and d_2 units, then $A = \frac{1}{2} d_1 \cdot d_2$

Example   **Find the area of the rhombus.**

$A = \frac{1}{2} d_1 d_2$ Area of rhombus

$= \frac{1}{2}(7)(9)$ $d_1 = 7$, and $d_2 = 9$

$= 31.5$ Simplify.

The area is 31.5 square meters.

Exercises

Find the area of each rhombus or kite.

1.

1640 in²

2.

400 cm²

3.

672 ft²

4.

338 cm²

5.

112 m²

6.

108 cm²

ALGEBRA Find x.

7. $A = 164$ ft²

x = 10 ft

8. $A = 340$ cm²

x = 17 cm

9. $A = 247.5$ mm²

x = 22 mm

Chapter 11   14   *Glencoe Geometry*

Left page

Areas of Trapezoids, Rhombi, and Kites

Find the area of each trapezoid, rhombus, or kite.

1. 31 m, 5 m, 16 m — **117.5 m²**

2. 34 cm, 11 cm — **187 cm²**

3. 2.4 in., 16.4 in. — **39.36 in²**

4. 6.5 ft, 8 ft, 21.5 ft, 17 ft, 12 ft — **112 ft²**

5. — **102 ft²**

6. 5 cm, 2 cm — **20 cm²**

ALGEBRA Find each missing length.

7. A trapezoid has base lengths of 19.5 and 24.5 centimeters with an area of 154 cm². What is the height of the trapezoid?
7 cm

8. One diagonal of a kite is twice as long as the other diagonal. If the area of the kite is 400 square meters, what are the lengths of the diagonals?
20 m, 40 m

9. A trapezoid has a height of 40 inches, a base of 15 inches, and an area of 2400 square inches. What is the length of the other base?
105 in.

10. DESIGN Mr. Hagarty used 16 congruent rhombi-shaped tiles to design the backsplash area above a kitchen sink. The length of the midsection of the design is 27 inches and the total area is 108 square inches.

a. Find the area of one rhombus.
6 3/4 in²

b. Find the length of each diagonal.
4 1/2 in., 3 in.

Right page

Areas of Trapezoids, Rhombi, and Kites

1. INTERIOR DESIGN The 20-by-20-foot square shows an office floor plan composed of three indoor gardens and one walkway, all congruent in shape. The gardens are centered around a 15-by-15 foot lounging area. What is the area of one of these gardens?

43.75 ft²

2. CUTOUTS A trapezoid is cut from a 6-inch-by-2-inch rectangle. The length of one base is 6 inches. What is the area of the trapezoid?
8 in²

3. SHARING Bernard has a birthday cake shaped like a kite. He needs to cut it into four pieces to share with three friends. He divides the cake as shown below. Which piece(s) is the largest? What is the area of the cake?
Pieces 3 and 4 are the largest; area of cake = 30 in²

4. HEXAGONS Heather makes a hexagon by attaching two trapezoids together as shown. What is the area of the hexagon?
20 cm, 15 cm, 30 cm, 15 cm, 10 cm
675 cm²

5. TILINGS Tile making often requires an artist to find clever ways of dividing a shape into several smaller, congruent shapes. Consider the isosceles trapezoid shown below.

a. Show how to divide the trapezoid into 3 congruent triangles. What is the area of each triangle?
√3/4 units²

b. Show how to divide the trapezoid into 4 congruent trapezoids. What is the area of each of the smaller trapezoids?
3√3/16 units²

Answers

NAME _____ DATE _____ PERIOD _____

11-3 Study Guide and Intervention

Areas of Circles and Sectors

Areas Of Circles The area of a circle is equal to π times the square of radius.

Area of a Circle	If a circle has an area of A square units and a radius of r units, then $A = \pi r^2$.

Example **Find the area of the circle p.**

$A = \pi r^2$ Area of a circle

$= \pi(6)^2$ $r = 6$

≈ 113.1 Use a calculator.

If $d = 12$ m, then $r = 6$ m.

The area of the circle is about 113.1 square meters.

Exercises

Find the area of each circle. Round to the nearest tenth.

1. **78.5 in²**

2. **314.2 m²**

3. **283.5 in.**

4. **95.0 ft²**

5. **6082.1 m²**

6. **380.1 in²**

Find the indicated measure. Round to the nearest tenth.

7. The area of a circle is 153.9 square centimeters. Find the diameter. **14.0 cm**

8. Find the diameter of a circle with an area of 490.9 square millimeters. **25.0 mm**

9. The area of a circle is 907.9 square inches. Find the radius. **17.0 in.**

10. Find the radius of a circle with an area of 63.6 square feet. **4.5 ft**

Chapter 11   19   Glencoe Geometry

NAME _____ DATE _____ PERIOD _____

11-2 Enrichment

Perimeters of Similar Figures

You have learned that if two figures are similar, the ratio of the lengths of the corresponding sides are equal. If two figures are similar, then their perimeters are also proportional to the scale factor between them.

Trapezoid II is k times larger than trapezoid I. Thus, its base is k times as large as that of trapezoid I and its height is k times as large as that of trapezoid I.

$\dfrac{\text{side of trapezoid II}}{\text{side of trapezoid I}} = \dfrac{ks_2}{s_2} = k$

$\dfrac{\text{perimeter trapezoid II}}{\text{perimeter trapezoid I}} = \dfrac{k(s_1 + s_2 + b_1 + b_2)}{s_1 + s_2 + b_1 + b_2} = k$

Perimeter $= s_1 + s_2 + b_1 + b_2$ Perimeter $= ks_1 + ks_2 + kb_1 + kb_2$
$= k(s_1 + s_2 + b_1 + b_2)$

Solve.

1. Trapezoid $ABCD \sim$ trapezoid $EFGH$. $EF = 10$, $GH = 8$, $HE = GF = 5$, and $AB = 5$. Find the perimeter of trapezoid $ABCD$.

perimeter trapezoid ABCD = 14

2. In the figure, $\overline{EF} \parallel \overline{AB}$ and the perimeter of trapezoid $ABCD$ is 56. Find the perimeter of trapezoid $EFCD$. Round to the nearest tenth.

perimeter of trapezoid EFCD = 37.3

3. Two similar trapezoids have perimeters of 37.5 feet and 150 feet. The length of a side of the smaller trapezoid is 10 feet. Find the length of the corresponding side of the larger trapezoid.

40 feet

4. Find the ratio of the perimeters of two similar trapezoids if the lengths of two corresponding sides of the trapezoids are 9 centimeters and 27 centimeters.

1:3

Chapter 11   18   Glencoe Geometry

Skills Practice page

NAME _____ DATE _____ PERIOD _____

11-3 Skills Practice

Areas of Circles and Sectors

Find the area of each circle.

1.

7 m

153.9 m²

2.

18 in.

254.5 in²

3.

10.5 m

346.4 m²

Find the indicated measure. Round to the nearest tenth.

4. The area of a circle is 132.7 square centimeters. Find the diameter.

13.0 cm

5. Find the diameter of a circle with an area of 1134.1 square millimeters. Find the diameter.

38.0 mm

6. The area of a circle is 706.9 square inches. Find the radius.

15.0 in.

7. Find the radius of a circle with an area of 2827.4 square feet.

30.0 ft

Find the area of each shaded sector. Round to the nearest tenth.

8.

A C
51° 2 m
B

1.8 m²

9.

J
K 130°
18 m
L

367.6 cm²

10.

D
243°
E
12.5 m
F

331.4 m²

16 cm

11. **GAMES** Jason wants to make a spinner for a new board game he invented. The spinner is a circle divided into 8 congruent pieces, what is the area of each piece to the nearest tenth?

25.1 cm²

Chapter 11   21   *Glencoe Geometry*

Study Guide page

NAME _____ DATE _____ PERIOD _____

11-3 Study Guide and Intervention *(continued)*

Areas of Circles and Sectors

Areas of Sectors A sector of a circle is a region bounded by a central angle and its intercepted arc.

Area of a Sector	If a sector of a circle has an area of A square units, a central angle measuring $x°$, and a radius of r units, then $A = \frac{x}{360} \cdot \pi r^2$.

Example **Find the area of the shaded sector.**

36° 5 in.

$A = \frac{x}{360} \cdot \pi r^2$

$= \frac{36}{360} \cdot \pi (5)^2$ $x = 36$ and $r = 5$

≈ 7.85 Use a calculator.

The area of the sector is about 7.85 square inches.

Exercises

Find the area of each shaded sector. Round to the nearest tenth.

1.

B
A 45°
3 ft
C

3.5 ft²

2.

J
L
100°
K
10 m

87.3 m²

3.

D F
20°
7 m
E

145.4 m²

4.

A
15°
C
20 ft
B

52.4 ft²

5.

K
36°
J
L
10 m

282.7 m²

6.

D
E
88°
7.5 cm
F

43.2 cm²

7. **SANDWICHES** For a party, Samantha wants to have finger sandwiches. She cuts sandwiches into circles. If she cuts each circle into three congruent pieces, what is the area of each piece?

2.5 in.

6.5 in²

Chapter 11   20   *Glencoe Geometry*

Answers

Chapter 11   A9   *Glencoe Geometry*

NAME _____ DATE _____ PERIOD _____

11-3 Word Problem Practice

Areas of Circles and Sectors

1. LOBBY The lobby of a bank features a large marble circular table. The diameter of circle is 15 feet.

15 ft

What is the area of the circular table? Round your answer to the nearest tenth.

176.7 ft²

2. PORTHOLES A circular window on a ship has a radius of 8 inches. What is the area of the window? Round your answer to the nearest hundredth.

201.06 in²

3. PEACE SYMBOL The symbol below, a circle separated into 3 equal sectors, has come to symbolize peace.

r

Suppose the circle has radius r. What is the area of each sector?

$\frac{1}{3}\pi r^2$ or $0.33\pi r^2$

4. SOUP CAN Julie needs to cover the top and bottom of a can of soup with construction paper to include in her art project. Each circle has a diameter of 7.5 centimeters. What is the total area of the can that Julie must cover?

88.4 cm²

5. POOL A circular pool is surrounded by a circular sidewalk. The circular sidewalk is 3 feet wide. The diameter of the sidewalk and pool is 26 feet.

Sidewalk

Pool

Diameter of sidewalk and pool = 26 ft

a. What is the diameter of the pool?

20 ft

b. What is the area of the sidewalk and pool?

169π ≈ 530.9 ft²

c. What is the area of the pool?

100π = 314.2 ft²

Chapter 11   23   *Glencoe Geometry*

NAME _____ DATE _____ PERIOD _____

11-3 Practice

Areas of Circles and Sectors

Find the area of each circle. Round to the nearest tenth.

1.

1.5 m

7.1 m²

2.

24 in.

452.4 in²

3.

4.5 cm

63.6 cm²

Find the indicated measure. Round to the nearest tenth.

4. The area of a circle is 3.14 square centimeters. Find the diameter. **2.0 cm**

5. Find the diameter of a circle with an area of 855.3 square millimeters. **33.0 mm**

6. The area of a circle is 201.1 square inches. Find the radius. **8.0 in.**

7. Find the radius of a circle with an area of 2290.2 square feet. **27.0 ft**

Find the area of each shaded sector. Round to the nearest tenth.

8.

A   C
37°
19 m
B

116.6 m²

9.

D
8°
F
6 in.
E

110.6 in²

10.

K
128°
L
J
10 cm

111.7 cm²

11. CLOCK Sadie wants to draw a clock face on a circular piece of cardboard. If the clock face has a diameter of 20 centimeters and is divided into congruent pieces so that each sector is 30°, what is the area of each piece?

26.2 cm²

Chapter 11   22   *Glencoe Geometry*

NAME _____ DATE _____ PERIOD _____

11-4 Study Guide and Intervention

Areas of Regular Polygons and Composite Figures

Areas of Regular Polygons In a regular polygon, the segment drawn from the center of the polygon perpendicular to the opposite side is called the **apothem**. In the figure at the right, AP is the apothem and AR is the radius of the circumscribed circle.

Area of a Regular Polygon	If a regular polygon has an area of A square units, a perimeter of P units, and an apothem of a units, then $A = \frac{1}{2}aP$.

Example 1 Verify the formula $A = \frac{1}{2}aP$ for the regular pentagon above.

For $\triangle RAS$, the area is

$A = \frac{1}{2}bh = \frac{1}{2}(RS)(AP)$. So the area of the pentagon is $A = 5\left(\frac{1}{2}\right)(RS)(AP)$. Substituting P for $5RS$ and substituting a for AP, then

$A = \frac{1}{2}aP$.

Example 2 Find the area of regular pentagon $RSTUV$ above if its perimeter is 60 centimeters.

First find the apothem.

The measure of central angle RAS is $\frac{360°}{5}$ or $72°$. Therefore, $m\angle RAP = 36$. The perimeter is 60, so $RS = 12$ and $RP = 6$.

$\tan m\angle RAP = \frac{RP}{AP}$

$\tan 36° = \frac{6}{AP}$

$AP = \frac{6}{\tan 36°}$

≈ 8.26

So, $A = \frac{1}{2}aP = \frac{1}{2}(60)(8.26)$ or 247.8.
The area is about 248 square centimeters.

Exercises

Find the area of each regular polygon. Round to the nearest tenth.

1. 14 m
84.9 m²

2. 10 in.
172.0 in²

3. 15 in.
225.0 in²

4. $5\sqrt{3}$ cm
259.8 cm²

5. 10 in.
482.8 in²

6. 10.9 m, 7.5 m
204.4 m²

Chapter 11   25   *Glencoe Geometry*

NAME _____ DATE _____ PERIOD _____

11-3 Enrichment

Perimeter of a Sector

You have learned how to find the area of a sector of a circle using a ratio of the circle and the area formula. Now you will learn how to find the perimeter of the sector of the circle.

The perimeter of the sector is the sum of the lengths of two radii and the length of its arc.

$P_{sector} = 2r + \text{length of } \overset{\frown}{AB}$

Step 1 Find the length of $\overset{\frown}{AB}$

The length of the arc is a section of the circumference. Multiply the ratio of the degree measure of the intercepted arc to 360° by the circumference of the circle.

Length of arc $= \frac{x}{360} \cdot 2(\pi)(r)$

Length of $\overset{\frown}{AB} = \frac{100}{360} \cdot 2(\pi)(6)$ $x = 100$ and $r = 6$

≈ 10.5 Use a calculator.

Step 2 Use the formula for the perimeter of a sector.

$P_{sector} = 2r + \text{length of } \overset{\frown}{AB}$

$\approx 2(6) + 10.5$

≈ 22.5

The perimeter of the sector is about 22.5 inches.

Exercises

Find the perimeter of the shaded sector. Round to the nearest tenth.

1. 50°, 8 m
23.0 m

2. 150°, 5 ft
23.1 ft

3. 170°, 15 cm
74.5 cm

4. 48°, 12.5 m
35.5 m

Chapter 11   24   *Glencoe Geometry*

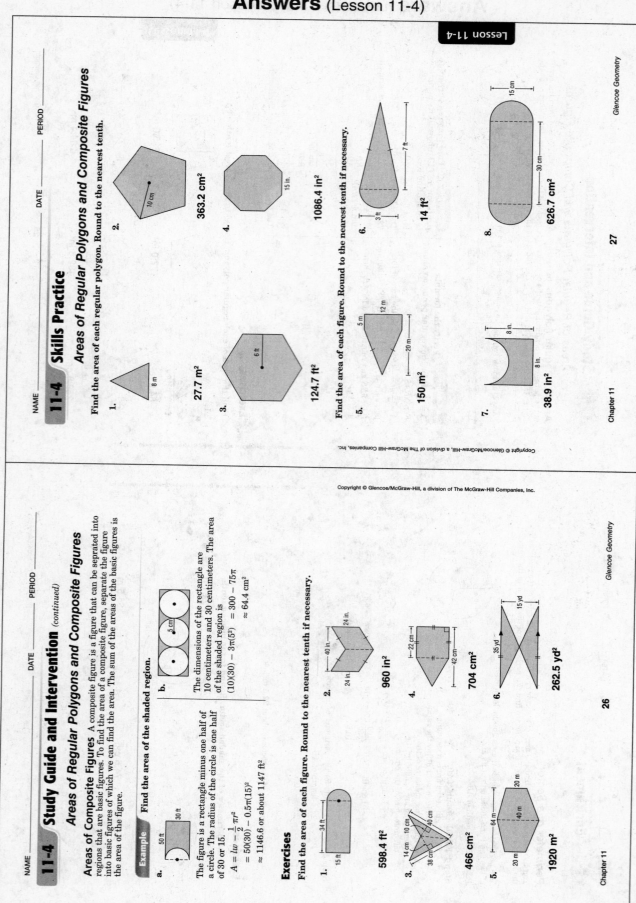

NAME _____ **DATE** _____ **PERIOD** _____

11-4 Skills Practice

Areas of Regular Polygons and Composite Figures

Find the area of each regular polygon. Round to the nearest tenth.

1. 8 m

   27.7 m²

2. 10 cm

   363.2 cm²

3. 6 ft

   124.7 ft²

4. 15 in.

   1086.4 in²

Find the area of each figure. Round to the nearest tenth if necessary.

5. 5 m, 12 m, 20 m

   150 m²

6. 3 ft, 7 ft

   14 ft²

7. 8 in., 8 in.

   38.9 in²

8. 15 cm, 30 cm

   626.7 cm²

Chapter 11   27   Glencoe Geometry

NAME _____ **DATE** _____ **PERIOD** _____

11-4 Study Guide and Intervention (continued)

Areas of Regular Polygons and Composite Figures

Areas of Composite Figures A composite figure is a figure that can be separated into regions that are basic figures. To find the area of a composite figure, separate the figure into basic figures of which we can find the area. The sum of the areas of the basic figures is the area of the figure.

Example Find the area of the shaded region.

a. 50 ft, 30 ft

b. 5 cm

The figure is a rectangle minus one half of a circle. The radius of the circle is one half of 30 or 15.

$A = lw - \frac{1}{2}\pi r^2$

$= 50(30) - 0.5\pi(15)^2$

≈ 1146.6 or about 1147 ft²

The dimensions of the rectangle are 10 centimeters and 30 centimeters. The area of the shaded region is

$(10)(30) - 3\pi(5^2) = 300 - 75\pi$

≈ 64.4 cm²

Exercises

Find the area of each figure. Round to the nearest tenth if necessary.

1. 34 ft, 15 ft

   598.4 ft²

2. 24 in., 40 in., 24 in.

   960 in²

3. 40 cm, 10 cm, 14 cm, 38 cm

   704 cm²

4. 22 cm, 42 cm

   466 cm²

5. 64 m, 40 m, 20 m, 20 m, 20 m

   1920 m²

6. 35 yd, 15 yd

   262.5 yd²

Chapter 11   26   Glencoe Geometry

NAME _____ DATE _____ PERIOD _____

11-4 Practice

Areas of Regular Polygons and Composite Figures

Find the area of each regular polygon. Round to the nearest tenth.

1.
14 cm

84.9 cm²

2.
7 m

178.0 m²

Find the area of each figure. Round to the nearest tenth if necessary.

3.
20 mm
20 mm

400 mm²

4.
38 ft
22 ft
22 ft

869.6 ft²

5.
9 m
7 m
7 m
23 m

143.8 m²

6.
20 in.
20 in.
13 in. 13 in.
30 in.

952.4 in²

7. **LANDSCAPING** One of the displays at a botanical garden is a koi pond with a walkway around it. The figure shows the dimensions of the pond and the walkway.

15 ft
7 ft
13 ft
35 ft

a. Find the area of the pond to the nearest tenth.
129.5 ft²

b. Find the area of the walkway to the nearest tenth.
572.2 ft²

NAME _____ DATE _____ PERIOD _____

11-4 Word Problem Practice

Areas of Regular Polygons and Composite Figures

1. **YIN-YANG SYMBOL** A well-known symbol from Chinese culture is the yin-yang symbol, shown below.

Suppose the large circle has radius r, the small circles have radius $\frac{r}{8}$, and the S-curve is two semicircles, each with radius $\frac{r}{2}$. In terms of r, what is the area of the black region?

$\dfrac{\pi r^2}{2}$

2. **PYRAMIDS** Martha's clubhouse is shaped like a square pyramid with four congruent equilateral triangles for its sides. All of the edges are 6 feet long. What is the total surface area of the clubhouse including the floor? Round your answer to the nearest hundredth.

98.35 ft²

3. **MINIATURE GOLF** The plan for a miniature golf hole is shown below. The right angle in the drawing is a central angle.

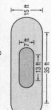
3 m
1.7 m

What is the area of the playing surface? Round your answer to the nearest hundredth of a square meter.
9.23 m²

4. **TRACK** A running track has an inner and outer edge. Both the inner and outer edges consist of two semicircles joined by two straight line segments. The straight line segments are 100 yards long. The radii of the inner edge semicircles are 25 yards each and the radii of the outer edge semicircles are 32 yards each. What is the area of the track? Round your answer to the nearest hundredth of a yard.

100 yd
25 yd

2653.50 yd²

5. **SEMICIRCLES** Bridget arranged three semicircles in the pattern shown.

The right triangle has side lengths 6, 8, and 10 inches.

a. What is the total area of the three semicircles? Round your answer to the nearest hundredth of a square inch.
78.54 in²

b. If the right triangle had side lengths $\sqrt{21}$, $\sqrt{79}$, and 10 inches, what would the total area of the three semicircles be? Round your answer to the nearest hundredth of a square inch.
78.54 in²

Lesson 11-4

NAME _____ DATE _____ PERIOD _____

11-5 Study Guide and Intervention

Areas of Similar Figures

Areas of Similar Figures If two polygons are similar, then their areas are proportional to the square of the scale factor between them.

Example $\triangle JKL \sim \triangle PQR$.
The area of $\triangle JKL$ is 40 square inches. Find the area of $\triangle PQR$.

Find the scale factor: $\dfrac{12}{10}$ or $\dfrac{6}{5}$.

The ratio of their areas is $\left(\dfrac{6}{5}\right)^2$.

$\dfrac{\text{area of } \triangle PQR}{\text{area of} \triangle JKL} = \left(\dfrac{6}{5}\right)^2$ Write a proportion.

$\dfrac{\text{area of } \triangle PQR}{40} = \dfrac{36}{25}$ Area of $\triangle JKL = 40$; $\left(\dfrac{6}{5}\right)^2 = \dfrac{36}{25}$

area of $\triangle PQR = \dfrac{36}{25} \cdot 40$ Multiply each side by 40.

area of $\triangle PQR = 57.6$ Simplify.

So the area of $\triangle PQR$ is 57.6 square inches.

Exercises

For each pair of similar figures, find the area of the shaded figure. Round to the nearest tenth if necessary.

1. **108 m²**

2. **180 in²**

3. **435.8 cm²**

4. **5152 ft²**

Chapter 11   31   *Glencoe Geometry*

NAME _____ DATE _____ PERIOD _____

11-4 Enrichment

Areas of Inscribed Polygons

A protractor can be used to inscribe a regular polygon in a circle. Follow the steps below to inscribe a regular nonagon in ⊙N.

Step 1 Find the degree measure of each of the nine congruent arcs. **40**

Step 2 Draw 9 radii to form 9 angles with the measure you found in Step 1. The radii will intersect the circle in 9 points.

Step 3 Connect the nine points to form the nonagon.

1. Find the length of one side of the nonagon to the nearest tenth of a centimeter. What is the perimeter of the nonagon? **2.5 cm, P = 22.5 cm**

2. Measure the distance from the center perpendicular to one of the sides of the nonagon. **3.4 cm**

3. What is the area of one of the nine triangles formed? **4.25 cm²**

4. What is the area of the nonagon? **38.25 cm²**

Make the appropriate changes in Steps 1–3 above to inscribe a regular pentagon in ⊙P. Answer each of the following.

5. Use a protractor to inscribe a regular pentagon in ⊙P.

6. What is the measure of each of the five congruent arcs? **72**

7. What is the perimeter of the pentagon to the nearest tenth of a centimeter? **21.0 cm**

8. What is the area of the pentagon to the nearest tenth of a centimeter? **30.5 cm²**

Chapter 11   30   *Glencoe Geometry*

NAME _____ DATE _____ PERIOD _____

Lesson 11-5

11-5 Skills Practice

Areas of Similar Figures

For each pair of similar figures, find the area of the shaded figure.

1.
11 m / 44 m
$A = 20$ m²

320 m²

2.
8.5 in. / 2 in.
$A = 34$ in²

Area = 1.9 in²

For each pair of similar figures, use the given areas to find the scale factor from the unshaded to the shaded figure. Then find x.

3.
21 m
$A = 4590$ m²
x
$A = 510$ m²

$\dfrac{1}{3}$; 7 m

4.
12 ft
$A = 360$ ft²
x
$A = 10$ ft²

6; 2 ft

5.
9.5 in.
$A = 71$ in²
x
$A = 16$ in²

$\sqrt{\dfrac{71}{16}}$; 4.5 in.

6.
14 ft
$A = 588$ ft²
x
$A = 272$ ft²

$\sqrt{\dfrac{68}{147}}$; 9.5 ft

7. **SCIENCE PROJECT** Matt has two posters for his science project. Each poster is a rectangle. The length of the larger poster is 11 inches. The length of the smaller poster is 6 inches. What is the area of the smaller poster if the larger poster is 93.5 square inches?

27.8 in²

Chapter 11   33   Glencoe Geometry

NAME _____ DATE _____ PERIOD _____

11-5 Study Guide and Intervention (continued)

Areas of Similar Figures

Scale Factors and Missing Measures in Similar Figures You can use the areas of similar figures to find the scale factor between them or a missing measure.

Example If $\square ABDC$ is similar to $\square FGJH$, find the value of x.

Let k be the scale factor between $\square ABDC$ and $\square FGJH$.

$\dfrac{\text{area } \square ABCD}{\text{area } \square FGJH} = k^2$ Theorem 11.1

$\dfrac{64}{49} = k^2$ Substitution

$\dfrac{8}{7} = k$ Take the positive square root of each side.

Use this scale factor to find the value of x.

$\dfrac{CD}{HJ} = k$

$\dfrac{10}{x} = \dfrac{8}{7}$ Substitution

$x = \dfrac{7}{8} \cdot 10$ or 8.75   Multiply each side by 10.

Exercises

For each pair of similar figures, use the given areas to find the scale factor from the unshaded to the shaded figure. Then find x.

1.
8 in.
$A = 54$ in²
x
$A = 216$ in²

$k = \dfrac{1}{2}$; $x = 16$ in.

2.
28 ft
$A = 296$ ft²
x ft
$A = 169$ ft²

$k = \sqrt{\dfrac{296}{169}}$; $x = 21.2$ ft

3.
21 cm
$A = 900$ cm²
x cm
$A = 300$ cm²

$k = \sqrt{3}$; $x = 12.1$

4.
7 ft
$A = 50$ ft²
x
$A = 30$ ft²

$k = \sqrt{\dfrac{5}{3}}$; $x = 5.4$ ft

Chapter 11   32   Glencoe Geometry

NAME _____ DATE _____ PERIOD _____

11-5 Word Problem Practice

Areas of Similar Figures

1. CHANGING DIMENSIONS A polygon has an area of 225 square meters. If the area is tripled, how does each side length change?

If the area is tripled, each side length will increase by a factor of $\sqrt{3}$.

2. CAKE Smith's Bakery is baking several large cakes for a community festival. The cakes consist of two geometrically similar shapes as shown. If 50 pieces of cake can be cut from the smaller cake, how many pieces of cake of the same size can be cut from the larger cake? Round to the nearest piece of cake.

Large cake — 5 ft, 4 ft

Smaller cake — 2 ft, 1.6 ft

313 pieces of cake

3. PINS Carla has a shirt with decorative pins in the shape of equilateral triangles. The pins come in two sizes. The larger pin has a side length that is three times longer than the smaller pin. If the area of the smaller pin is 6.9 square centimeters, what is the approximate area of the larger pin?

62.1 cm²

4. FOUNTAIN A local park has two fountains in the shape of similar trapezoids as shown.

Large fountain — 100 ft
Small fountain — 40 ft

A cement company charges $1000 to pour the cement needed to go under the smaller fountain. How much should the town budget for the cement for both fountains? Explain.

The ratio of the lengths of sides is 2.5, so the ratio of the areas should be $(2.5)^3$ or 15,625. The cost of the larger fountain should be times more than the small fountain, or $15,625. The total cost should be $15,625.

5. SCULPTURE An artist creates metal sculptures in the shape of regular octagons. The side length of the larger sculpture is 7 inches, and the area of the base of the smaller sculpture is 19.28 square inches.

a. What is the side length of the smaller sculpture?

2 inches

b. The artist is going to pack the sculptures in a circular box to take them to an art show. Will the larger sculpture fit in a circular box with a 15-inch diameter? Explain your reasoning.

No, the larger sculpture has an apothem of about 8.5 inches. This means that the octagonal shape of the larger sculpture is about 17 inches across. This is greater than the diameter of the box.

NAME _____ DATE _____ PERIOD _____

11-5 Practice

Areas of Similar Figures

For each pair of similar figures, find the area of the shaded figure.

1. 20 in., 30 in., $A = 200 \text{ in}^2$

450 in²

2. 16 m, 3 m, $A = 38 \text{ m}^2$

1.3 m²

For each pair of similar figures, use the given areas to find the scale factor from the unshaded to the shaded figure. Then find x.

3. x m, 8 m, $A = 50 \text{ m}^2$, $A = 72 \text{ m}^2$

$k = \dfrac{6}{5}; x = 6.7$ m

4. x cm, 7 cm, $A = 70 \text{ cm}^2$, $A = 30 \text{ cm}^2$

$k = \sqrt{\dfrac{7}{3}}; x = 10.7$ cm

5. x ft, 8 ft, $A = 16 \text{ ft}^2$, $A = 64 \text{ ft}^2$

$k = \dfrac{1}{2}; x = 4$ ft

6. 9 cm, x cm, $A = 39 \text{ cm}^2$, $A = 13 \text{ cm}^2$

$k = \sqrt{\dfrac{1}{3}}; x = 5.2$ cm

7. ARCHERY A target consists of two concentric similar octagons. The outside octagon has a side length of 2 feet and an area of 19.28 square feet. If the inside octagon has a side length of 1.5 feet, what is the area of the inside octagon?

10.8 ft²

NAME _____ DATE _____ PERIOD _____

11-5 Enrichment

Areas of Similar Figures

You have learned that to find the area of a composite figure, you find the area of each basic figure and then use the Area Addition Postulate. You have also learned that if two figures are similar, then their areas are proportional to the square of the scale factor between them.

You can find the area of similar composite figures using this knowledge.

Find the area of composite figure B.

Step 1: Find the area of composite figure A.

Area of rectangle = (3 ft)(7 ft) = 21 ft²

Area of trapezoid = $\frac{1}{2}$ (6 ft)(10 ft + 3 ft) = 39 ft²

Area of composite figure A = 21 ft² + 39 ft² = 60 ft².

Step 2: Use scale factor to find the area of composite figure B.

$$\text{area composite figure A} = \left(\frac{7}{4}\right)^2$$
$$\text{area composite figure B} = \frac{49}{16}$$
$$= \frac{49}{16}$$
$$\frac{60 \text{ ft}^2}{\text{area composite figure B}} = \frac{49}{16}$$
$$\text{area composite figure B} = 60 \cdot \frac{16}{49} = 19.6 \text{ ft}^2$$

So the area of composite figure B is about 19.6 square feet.

Solve.

1. Composite figure A is similar to composite figure B. Find the area of composite figure B.

396 in²

2. Jim is making a scale model of his rectangular backyard and circular pool. If the scale factor is 1:20, what is the area of his model? **about 2.27 ft²**

3. Composite figure A is similar to composite figure B. Find the value of x in composite figure B.

6 ft

4. Composite figure A and composite figure B are similar. The length of the sides of composite figure A is two-thirds the length of the sides of composite figure B. If the area of composite figure A is 240 cm², find the area of composite figure B.

540 cm²

Answers

Chapter 11 Assessment Answer Key

Quiz 1 (Lessons 11-1 and 11-2)
Page 39

1. _____ **33.8 in²** _____

2. _____ **160 in²** _____

3. _____ **61.3 m²** _____

4. _____ **350 ft²** _____

5. _____ **b = 10 cm; h = 20 cm** _____

Quiz 2 (Lesson 11-3)
Page 39

1. _____ **380.1 cm²** _____

2. _____ **153.9 ft²** _____

3. _____ **14.0 in²** _____

4. _____ **422.2 cm²** _____

5. _____ **5.64 ft** _____

Quiz 3 (Lesson 11-4)
Page 40

1. _____ **166.3 cm²** _____

2. _____ **1089.8 in²** _____

3. _____ **198 m²** _____

4. _____ **26.3 in²** _____

5. _____ **295 ft²** _____

Quiz 4 (Lesson 11-5)
Page 40

1. _____ **1843.2 m²** _____

2. _____ **2.53 in²** _____

3. _____ **13.1 in.** _____

4. _____ **3.2 cm** _____

5. _____ **5 in²** _____

Mid-Chapter Test
Page 41

Part I

1. ___ **D** ___

2. ___ **F** ___

3. ___ **B** ___

4. ___ **G** ___

Part II

5. _____ **1385.4 m²** _____

6. _____ **120 m²** _____

7. _____ **21.1 in²** _____

8. _____ **10 ft** _____

9. _____ **14 in.** _____

Chapter 11 Assessment Answer Key

Vocabulary Test
Page 42

1. _____ $A = \pi r^2$ _____

2. _____ $A = \frac{1}{2}bh$ _____

3. _____ $A = \frac{1}{2}h(b_1 + b_2)$ _____

4. _____ $A = \frac{1}{2}Pa$ _____

5. _____ $A = \frac{N}{360}\pi r^2$ _____

6. _____ sector of a circle _____

7. _____ base of the parallelogram _____

8. _____ apothem _____

9. _____ A line drawn from the center of a regular polygon perpendicular to a side. _____

10. _____ The perpendicular distance between the bases of a trapezoid. _____

Form 1
Page 43

1. __ D __

2. __ G __

3. __ A __

4. __ G __

5. __ C __

6. __ J __

7. __ A __

8. __ H __

Page 44

9. __ D __

10. __ H __

11. __ C __

12. __ F __

13. __ B __

14. __ F __

15. __ A __

B: __ 7.6 units² __

Answers

Chapter 11 Assessment Answer Key

Form 2A
Page 45

Page 46

Form 2B
Page 47

Page 48

1. __C__

2. __F__

3. __B__

4. __G__

5. __A__

6. __F__

7. __A__

8. __F__

9. __C__

10. __G__

11. __D__

12. __H__

13. __B__

14. __H__

15. __C__

B: __227.3 in²__

1. __B__

2. __J__

3. __A__

4. __H__

5. __C__

6. __G__

7. __B__

8. __H__

9. __C__

10. __G__

11. __C__

12. __F__

13. __D__

14. __G__

15. __A__

B: __536.3 in²__

Chapter 11 Assessment Answer Key

Form 2C
Page 49

Page 50

1. 173.2 cm²

2. 30.3 in²

3. 45 m

4. 46.5 cm²

5. 7.5 in²

6. 26.3 cm²

7. 80 ft²

8. 32 in²

9. 64.1 cm²

10. 1.9 in²

11. 42 cm²

12. 89.7 m²

13. $b = 25$ m; $h = 17$ m

14. 14 mm and 7 mm

15. 9.0 ft

16. 281.3 m²

17. 180 cm²

18. 184.3 cm²

B: 20 m

Answers

Chapter 11 Assessment Answer Key

Page 52

1. ___76.2 cm²___

2. ___78 in²___

3. ___30 m___

4. ___86 cm²___

5. ___7.2 ft²___

6. ___375 cm²___

7. ___31.5 in²___

8. ___36 in²___

9. ___584.6 cm²___

10. ___569.7 cm²___

11. ___189 cm²___

12. ___2.3 m²___

13. ___$b = 16$ m; $h = 20$ m___

14. ___45 mm and 15 mm___

15. ___18 ft___

16. ___126.8 m²___

17. ___86.4 cm²___

18. ___34.8 in²___

B: ___21 m___

Chapter 11 Assessment Answer Key

Form 3
Page 53   **Page 54**

1. _____41.6 cm²_____   11. _____23.7 in²_____

2. _____49 in²_____   12. _____24.3 cm²_____

3. _____20.2 m²_____

4. _____63 cm²_____   13. _____23.0 units²_____

                                         14. _____$b = 16.6$ m; $h = 4.15$ m_____

5. _____30.6 units²_____   15. _____68 mm and 34 mm_____

6. _____18 cm²_____   16. _____1.6 ft_____

                                         17. _____97.9 in²_____

7. _____336 m²_____

8. _____695.3 m²_____   B: _____17.4 cm²_____

9. _____90.8 in²_____

10. _____239.0 mm²_____

Answers

Chapter 11 Assessment Answer Key

Extended-Response Test, Page 55
Scoring Rubric

Score	General Description	Specific Criteria
4	**Superior** A correct solution that is supported by well-developed, accurate explanations	• Shows thorough understanding of *using formulas to find the areas of parallelograms, triangles, rhombi, trapezoids, regular polygons, circles, irregular figures, and segments and sectors of circles.* • Uses appropriate strategies to solve problems. • Written explanations are exemplary. • Graphs are accurate and appropriate. • Goes beyond requirements of some or all problems.
3	**Satisfactory** A generally correct solution, but may contain minor flaws in reasoning or computation	• Shows understanding of *using formulas to find the areas of parallelograms, triangles, rhombi, trapezoids, regular polygons, circles, irregular figures, and segments and sectors of circles.* • Uses appropriate strategies to solve problems. • Computations are mostly correct. • Written explanations are effective. • Graphs are mostly accurate and appropriate. • Satisfies all requirements of all problems.
2	**Nearly Satisfactory** A partially correct interpretation and/or solution to the problem	• Shows partial understanding of most of *using formulas to find the areas of parallelograms, triangles, rhombi, trapezoids, regular polygons, circles, irregular figures, and segments and sectors of circles.* • May not use appropriate strategies to solve problems. • Computations are mostly correct. • Written explanations are satisfactory. • Graphs are mostly accurate. • Satisfies the requirements of most of the problems.
1	**Nearly Unsatisfactory** A correct solution with no supporting evidence or explanation	• Final computation is correct. • No written explanations or work is shown to substantiate the final computation. • Graphs may be accurate but lack detail or explanation. • Satisfies minimal requirements of some of the problems.
0	**Unsatisfactory** An incorrect solution indicating no mathematical understanding of the concept or task, or no solution is given	• Shows little or no understanding of *using formulas to find the areas of parallelograms, triangles, rhombi, trapezoids, regular polygons, circles, irregular figures, and segments and sectors of circles.* • Does not use appropriate strategies to solve problems. • Computations are incorrect. • Written explanations are unsatisfactory. • Graphs are inaccurate or inappropriate. • Does not satisfy the requirements of the problems. • No answer may be given.

Chapter 11 Assessment Answer Key

Extended-Response Test, Page 55
Sample Answers

In addition to the scoring rubric found on page A24, the following sample answers may be used as guidance in evaluating open-ended assessment items.

1a. A 30°-60°-90° triangle can be used to find the altitude, $x\sqrt{3}$, and $\overline{PT}$, x. The hypotenuse of $\triangle PQT$ is $2x$ or 14. So, $x = 7$, the altitude is $7\sqrt{3}$, and base $PT = 7$. Since the height and base of parallelogram $PQRS$ are known, the area can be calculated.

1b. The base is $7 + 14$ or 21 and the height is $7\sqrt{3}$. $A = (21)(7\sqrt{3}) \approx 254.6$ in^2

2a. Use the Pythagorean Theorem to find the height of the rhombus. $6^2 + 8^2 = 10^2$, so the height is 8 cm. Then use $A = bh$; 80 cm^2.

2b. By using the ratios of a 30°-60°-90° triangle, the altitude of the trapezoid is $4\sqrt{3}$ cm and the base of $\triangle MNQ$ is 4 cm. The longer base of the trapezoid is $4 + 11$ or 15 cm. Since $A = \frac{1}{2}h(b_1 + b_2)$, the area is $\frac{1}{2}(4\sqrt{3})(11 + 15)$ or 90.1 cm^2.

2c. The area of the circle is 36π. The area of the hexagon is $A = \frac{1}{2}aP$. Since a regular hexagon can be divided into six equilateral triangles, use the 30°-60°-90° triangle ratios to find a and the length of one side of the hexagon. So, $a = 3\sqrt{3}$ in., each side is 6 in., and $P = 36$ in. By substitution, the area of the hexagon is 93.5 in^2. The area of the shaded region is $36\pi - 93.5 \approx 19.6$ in^2.

3. A similar trapezoid with an area four times the area of the one shown will increase the lengths of the sides by the same factor. For the area to quadruple, the length of the sides must double. Therefore, the height of the new trapezoid and one of the bases must become $2x$, while the length of the other base must become $2(x + 1)$ or $2x + 2$.

Answers

Chapter 11 Assessment Answer Key

Standardized Test Practice
Page 56   Page 57

9. Ⓐ Ⓑ Ⓒ ●

1. Ⓐ ● Ⓒ Ⓓ

10. Ⓕ Ⓖ ● Ⓙ

2. Ⓕ ● Ⓗ Ⓙ

11. Ⓐ Ⓑ ● Ⓓ

3. Ⓐ Ⓑ ● Ⓓ

12. ● Ⓖ Ⓗ Ⓙ

13.

			1	5
	⊘	⊘	⊘	
⊙	⊙	⊙	⊙	⊙
⓪	⓪	⓪	⓪	⓪
①	①	①	●	①
②	②	②	②	②
③	③	③	③	③
④	④	④	④	④
⑤	⑤	⑤	⑤	●
⑥	⑥	⑥	⑥	⑥
⑦	⑦	⑦	⑦	⑦
⑧	⑧	⑧	⑧	⑧
⑨	⑨	⑨	⑨	⑨

4. Ⓕ ● Ⓗ Ⓙ

5. Ⓐ Ⓑ Ⓒ ●

14.

1	1	2	.	5
	⊘	⊘	⊘	
⊙	⊙	⊙	●	⊙
⓪	⓪	⓪	⓪	⓪
●	●	①	①	①
②	②	●	②	②
③	③	③	③	③
④	④	④	④	④
⑤	⑤	⑤	⑤	●
⑥	⑥	⑥	⑥	⑥
⑦	⑦	⑦	⑦	⑦
⑧	⑧	⑧	⑧	⑧
⑨	⑨	⑨	⑨	⑨

6. Ⓕ ● Ⓗ Ⓙ

7. Ⓐ ● Ⓒ Ⓓ

8. Ⓕ Ⓖ ● Ⓙ

15. _____25.4; 16.8_____

16. _____109; 71; 4_____

17. _____312.6 mph; 7.4°
west of due south_____

18. _____36; 36; 25; 84.5_____

19. _____$X'(0, -3)$,
$Y'(-4, -7)$,
$Z'(5, -4)$_____

20. _____$m\angle TRU = 94$,
$m\angle URV = 39$,
$m\angle VRW = 47$_____

21. _____15 in._____

22. a. _____720_____

   b. _____139.1 units^2_____

Answers